THE END OF AGE

Tom Kirkwood was Britain's first Professor of Biological
Gerontology at the University of Manchester and is now Professor
of Medicine and head of the Department of Gerontology at the
University of Newcastle. Educated at the Universities of
Cambridge and Oxford, he began research on ageing in 1974, first
at the National Institute for Biological Standards and Control and
subsequently at the National Institute for Medical Research. He
has published more than 160 scientific papers on a wide range of
subjects connected to human ageing and is internationally
renowned for his 'disposable soma' theory of ageing, which now
shapes and inspires much of the research in this field. Tom
Kirkwood has served on numerous scientific committees and is on
the editorial board of eight international academic journals in the
life sciences and medicine.

THE END OF AGE

Tom Kirkwood

P

PROFILE BOOKS

THE BBC IN ASSOCIATION WITH PROFILE BOOKS LTD

First published in 2001 by
Profile Books Ltd
58A Hatton Garden
London EC1N 8LX
www.profilebooks.co.uk

10 9 8 7 6 5 4 3 2 1

Typeset in Bembo by
MacGuru
info@macguru.org.uk
Printed and bound in Great Britain by
Bookmarque Ltd, Croydon, Surrey

ISBN 1 86197 277 6

For Louise

Contents

Preface

This short book began life with an invitation from the BBC to deliver the 2001 Reith Lectures on the subject of ageing, as seen from the perspective of science. Recognition of the challenge to science and society from the revolution in longevity could not be more timely. Dramatic increases in life expectancy are shaking the structure of societies around the world and profoundly altering our perceptions of life and death. Not only are we living longer, but the evidence of recent decades shows that old age itself is being transformed. The latest cohorts of older people are in significantly better health than their predecessors, and this trend appears to be continuing. At the same time, a revolution is taking place in the life sciences which already shows us that many of our deeply ingrained preconceptions about ageing are wrong. We are not programmed to die but to survive, and we are beginning to discover much about the body's cellular survival mechanisms that, in time, we will be able to use to extend the years of good quality life.

Paradoxically, this time of increased life span and increased understanding of the ageing process is marred by the extraordinary obsession we have with youth, which seems to exclude any true appreciation of age. It is of the highest possible priority for the future shape and even stability of our society that we look afresh at what is happening. There is a great deal that needs to be done to develop a more positive attitude to the challenge of ageing if the successes of the past, which have made our longer lives possible, are not to turn sour. The scourge of ageism is hugely under-recognised and it is high time that we began a systematic inquiry into what needs to be done to accommodate the greatly increased numbers of older people within our society on an equal footing.

The book is divided into three parts. The first contains the texts of the five Reith Lectures delivered in London, New York, Edinburgh, Stoke-on-Trent and Newcastle. As is now customary, each lecture was delivered to an audience and followed by active discussion and argument. The lectures and ensuing discussions were broadcast on BBC Radio 4 and the BBC World Service, as well as being available through the BBC website (www.bbc.co.uk/radio4/reith2001). Additionally, the website was available for on-line debate about the theme of the lectures. I am grateful to all who took part (and continue to take part) in all facets of this highly interactive process. I only wish that greater strides had been made in extending internet usage to a greater proportion of older people.

The second part of the book is a more detailed discussion of a selection from the science stories that have been making headlines about research into ageing over the past year. It appears impossible for advances in such research to be reported without a phrase like 'fountain of youth' creeping into the body, if not the headline, of the article. My aim here is to give a more measured appraisal of research that is scientifically very exciting and which will unquestionably take us forward in our quest to improve the health and quality of later life, but which should not cause insurance companies to stop selling their annuity policies just yet.

The third part of the book, reproduced with kind permission of Orion Books, is a work of fiction – a short story written to explore the implications of a world in which science has found a way to postpone ageing indefinitely. I was prompted to write this story by the many journalists and interviewers who have asked what the world will be like if ageing research produces 'the breakthrough'. As will be clear from the story, as well as other parts of the book, I do not think such a breakthrough is imminent. Nevertheless, from a biological perspective, there is nothing necessary or inevitable about ageing, and I believe there is no fundamental barrier to what might one day be achieved. The science on which my future world is based is, I believe, a plausible scenario. The story first appeared as an epilogue to my book *Time of Our Lives: The Science of Human Ageing* published in 1999 and now available as a Phoenix paperback. This book gives a fuller discussion of the science and social issues raised by an ageing population than can be attempted here.

When I accepted the invitation from Helen Boaden (Controller, BBC Radio 4) to deliver the Reith Lectures, I had little idea of how much work was involved behind the scenes, and I am immensely grateful first and foremost to Gwyneth Williams, whose wise counsel and insight guided me from start to finish. Sue Lawley was superb as presenter and chair of the discussions. Charles Sigler, Marion Greenwood, Sheila Cook, Smita Patel, Sarah Orchardson, Liz Hamilton, Adele Cross, Lucinda Webb and many others helped in various ways to make the process both efficient and fun. My secretary Sharon Denley has, with her usual skill and cheerfulness, held the threads together at a time when many other activities demanded attention. Andrew Franklin, my editor, gave helpful advice at all stages of producing the book, and Felicity Bryan, my agent, was a very great help. I must thank colleagues, friends and students too numerous to list for the stimulus of working and arguing together about this most intriguing of fields, as well as the various bodies that have funded my work. But my greatest debt without doubt is to my wife Louise.

Part I

The Reith Lectures

I

Brave Old World

Delivered at the Royal Institution, London

Never in human history has a population so wilfully and deliberately defied nature by surviving as long as the present generation. We face a revolution in longevity which is shaking the foundations of societies around the world and profoundly altering our attitudes to life and death. At the same time, science has made hitherto undreamed-of advances in human biology. The explosive force of these two revolutions coming together lies at the heart of my series of Reith Lectures, as it has been at the heart of my work over the last decade. Science has new things to tell us about the process of ageing. Now we know that ageing is no longer inevitable or necessary.

It is particularly fitting that the first lecture in a series that will explore the revolution in human longevity should be given at the Royal Institution. This establishment, founded in 1799, has played a pioneering role in science and technology. It was here, exactly two hundred years ago, that the young Humphry Davy was appointed to arrange scientific demonstrations for the public. Davy's demonstrations were spectacular events, often noisy and dangerous, and there is delicious irony in the fact that Davy's best-known legacy is the miner's safety lamp, expressly designed to prevent explosions from occurring. My adoptive city of Newcastle upon Tyne, famously associated in earlier times with coal mining, has had good reason to bless the life-preserving qualities of the Davy lamp.

Although the theatre will not reverberate tonight to the fizz and bang of Davy's demonstrations, the revolution in longevity is, in its own way, more spectacular. Davy's safety lamp was but one contribution in a process that has led, in the eight or so generations between his time and ours, to more than a doubling in the average length of life.

Life expectancy at the start of the nineteenth century was scarcely forty years. Some of course lived to a good old age but they were a distinct minority. Davy himself died at fifty-one. Life expectancy in the United Kingdom today is around seventy-five years for a man and eighty years for a woman, and it is still getting longer.

Over the course of the last half-century, life expectancy has continued to increase steadily by two years per decade. It is almost as if for each decade we have lived, we have gained an extra 20 per cent free. The real calculations are more complicated than this because the figures I have given are for life expectancy *at birth*. Working out how our individual expectation of life has changed must take account not only of changes in death rates but also how long we have lived already. Nevertheless, it is striking that it is the death rates of the older age groups that are presently showing the greatest declines. It is these older age groups – those over eighty-five years – who now constitute the fastest growing segment of the population.

A phrase often used to describe what is happening is 'demographic change'. This dry expression masks the greatest *triumph* that our species has achieved. I emphasise the word triumph because, as we shall see, there are far too many people who like to dwell on the dangers inherent in the longevity revolution without celebrating the progress that has opened these new horizons. The demographic change has two causes, both of which are reasons for joy. Firstly, people on the average are living longer than at any time in human history. Secondly, because fewer children are dying, birth rates are tumbling across much of the planet. No longer do parents need to raise large families as insurance against child mortality. These two factors – longer lives and smaller families – are signals of our success in taming the age-old scourge of premature, preventable death.

We soon learn in life, however, that success is not an end in itself but brings new challenges. These new challenges are often more daunting than those that came before, and so it is with longevity. With our longer life spans we are entering uncharted territory in which the challenges for individuals and societies are formidable. They are formidable not least because we cherish extra-ordinarily negative stereotypes of the ageing process. The stereotypes have, if anything, grown more negative as life expectancy has increased. Survival to old age is less of an achievement and as life has become more secure, the inevitability of eventual ageing seems more of an affront.

Like it or not, the world is changing, and changing fast. The demographic transition that occurred over the last century in the developed countries is in train in most of the developing world. The technologies to enhance survival – vaccines, antibiotics, water purification systems, electricity, and so on – are already at hand and require only effective implementation. Whereas just 1 per cent of the world's population was aged sixty-five and above a century ago, this figure has already risen seven-fold and will rise to around 20 per cent by the middle of the twenty-first century. In the UK today, 85 per cent of newborns can expect to celebrate their sixty-fifth birthday. Those now reaching sixty-five can expect to survive a further sixteen years if they are a man and nineteen years if they are a woman.

It is no surprise that the number of older people is on the increase. That, after all, is where the drive to avoid death has led us. What is surprising, however, is that the nature of old age itself seems to be changing. If you have the impression, as many do, that old people, like policemen, are getting younger all the time, it is not just that you yourself are getting older. In many respects today's seventy-year-olds are like the sixty-year-olds of a generation or two ago.

The starkest feature of ageing – its hallmark, in fact – is that the risk of falling ill and dying increases inexorably as we get older. This unwelcome principle was first cast into mathematical form in 1825 by Benjamin Gompertz, a pioneer of actuarial science. What Gompertz found was that adult mortality rates increased exponentially with age, like compound interest. In effect, your risk of dying doubles with every additional eight years that you live. Were Gompertz alive today he would find that this fundamental property has not altered but that death rates have fallen. It is as if the capital on which his compound interest was acting had grown less. The most significant trend affecting longevity in developed countries today is the remarkable and continuing decline in the death rates of older people.

If you had asked most experts just a couple of decades

ago what they would have predicted for the patterns of mortality at the end of the century, the answer you would have received was that the continuing declines in preventable, early mortality would have revealed ever more clearly the rigid, immutable pattern of mortality associated with intrinsic ageing. The medical term to describe the change from a pattern of mortality dominated by acute infectious disease to a pattern in which the chronic degenerative diseases play the major role is the 'epidemiological transition'. Linked to this is the idea of 'mortality substitution'. Put bluntly, mortality substitution means that you have to die of something. If you are spared early death from infections such as tuberculosis and typhoid, you fall prey instead to conditions such as heart disease, cancer or stroke. Not only does ageing make each of these diseases more prevalent individually, but you are also more likely to experience a multiplicity of conditions. Many diseases, disabilities or just plain causes of frailty, like thinning bones, weakening muscles and diminishment of the senses, are intimately linked to the ageing process. When we speak loosely of a person dying of 'old age' we have in mind the notion of multiple system failure. The actual cause of death may be quite specific but if it had not been this particular cause today, it would have been something else tomorrow. It is the idea that this intrinsic deterioration is something fixed or immutable – to be revealed more clearly as we peel away one preventable cause of death after another – that has come to be seen in a new and questioning light. The new realisation is that science no longer dictates that our bodies have to wear themselves out and die according to some preordained plan.

Death rates are going down, life expectancy is going up and the maximum life span is rising too. We saw in 1997 that the world record for reliably documented life span was extended in spectacular fashion by Jeanne Calment, who died at the remarkable age of 122 years and 5 months. It may be some time before Jeanne Calment's record is broken, but broken it will be. Where will it all end? More to the point, if we heed the doom-mongers who hark on about the 'burden' of the elderly, will it all end in tears?

To be able to answer this question in anything other than hand-waving fashion, we need some harder facts. In particular, we need to understand a great deal more about the ageing process. It is fortunate, but by no means coincidental, that the revolution in longevity is accompanied by an equally unprecedented revolution in the life sciences. As a result of the astonishing advances made over the last decades – advances in understanding the basic chemistry of life, advances in genetics and genome research, and advances in studying and manipulating individual cells both inside the body and out of it – it is now reasonably certain that we will soon understand the ageing process in much closer detail than we do at present. Already, we can use scientific insights to overturn many preconceptions – or, should I say, misconceptions – about why and how we age.

The commonest misconceptions about the ageing process are that we age because in some fundamental sense we *cannot* survive for longer, or that we are *programmed* to die because this is necessary to make way for the next generation. Neither of these ideas is correct. The glum fatalism that says that we cannot hold ourselves together for longer is contradicted by the existence of organisms that manage the amazing feat of living indefinitely without intrinsic deterioration. Sea anemones and freshwater hydra are examples of species that show no signs of ageing. There are also several species of fish and giant tortoise that live considerably longer than us, and which age much more slowly. We shall see in a later lecture that we can learn quite a lot about the ageing process by comparing species that live their lives at different rates.

The second misconception – that we are programmed to die – is remarkably tenacious. We seem to be psychologically – perhaps emotionally – tuned to seek a purpose in the biology of ageing, but this tuning leads us astray. Sigmund Freud illustrated this fallacy perfectly in his key treatise 'Beyond the Pleasure Principle,' in which he balanced the life-instinct, *eros*, against the death instinct, *thanatos*, of the organism, drawing upon contemporary thinking about the biology of ageing to offer a quasi-scientific explanation for the death wish. I am frequently reminded of this as I drive home in a part of the country that is densely populated with rabbits. Rabbits, as we know, have a highly developed *eros*. But time and again they dart into the road at the last possible moment of my approach, and I feel sure they have made the mistake of reading too far into their Freud.

We now understand that our bodies are not programmed with some unavoidable sell-by date; we are not programmed to die. As I said at the start of this lecture, ageing is neither inevitable nor necessary. Indeed, the more we learn about how we age, the more we come to realise that we are programmed for survival. It is by understanding why this programming falls short of allowing us to survive indefinitely that we may learn deep lessons that we can turn to our advantage.

The lie to the suggestion that we must limit our survival in order to make way for the next generation is that it is only in the last few human generations that survival into old age has been anything other than a rarity. We are not alone in this. Rabbits, mice and small birds age as we do, but in these species ageing is even less likely to be seen, except in captivity. Life in the natural world is brutish and short. The vast majority of wild animals die young from accidents (including unadvisedly running under cars), infections, predation, starvation and cold. If our evolutionary ancestors had a problem with survival it was that they had too little of it, and not too much.

Once we relinquish the idea of a programmed death, we can begin to make better sense of our ageing. We do this by taking a fresh look at the fact that our ancestors tended to live short lives and by asking ourselves, in those circumstances, how much effort should their bodies have directed at maintenance and repair. The human body is astonishingly well programmed to cope with a huge variety of challenges to its integrity on a daily basis. Many of these challenges are at the sub-microscopic level and the body's defence involves an extensive repertoire of cellular and molecular protection systems. The price we pay for these protection systems is that they require energy, and this is often in limited supply. When survival is uncertain because of the many hazards of the environment it is better not to squander effort on a greater level of bodily maintenance than is needed, but to attend instead to the all-important biological imperative of begetting and raising offspring. If, to a rough approximation, the average life span of our ancestors was around thirty years and only a tiny percentage survived to seventy years, then a body which held itself together for three score years and ten would do just fine.

When we understand that we age because our ancestral genes programmed our survival but placed a limited priority on long-term maintenance and repair, we get some rather clear insights into the processes that lead to the frailty and illnesses of old age.

The first and most encouraging message is that as soon as we recognise that we are programmed not to die, but to survive, we can see that the ageing process is malleable. Ageing comes about through the gradual build-up of unrepaired faults in the cells and tissues of our bodies as we live our lives, not as a result of some active mechanism for death and destruction. If we can discover the nature of these faults, we can hope to slow their accumulation. There is good reason to believe that the improved health and survival of older people today at least partly reflects the fact that the kinder conditions of present-day living have alleviated some of the burden of faults. If we can understand the protection systems with which we are already endowed, and enhance their performance, we may be able to do much better.

Although the malleability of the ageing process offers exciting grounds for hope, as will be described in a later lecture, we should guard against unrealistic expectations of a 'quick fix'. Ageing is a complicated process with multiple causes affecting every organ of the body. Its complexity will make it refractory to change and we need to temper our optimism with a considerable degree of determination. We have seen already how frustratingly slow and difficult it has been to take the sting from heart disease, cancer and stroke. To get excited about potential 'fountains of youth' and life spans of 200 years or more is not only to indulge in fanciful and unrealistic speculation, it also shows what a long way we still have to go to get the challenges of the longevity revolution into proper perspective.

The paradox about the longevity revolution, and its greatest inherent danger, is that we find ourselves in the present situation without having thought very much, until recently, about the kind of world we are creating. It is easy to win support for saving lives. Davy's safety lamp, Jenner's triumph of inoculation against smallpox, Fleming's discovery of penicillin – these are unquestionable gains. It is relatively easy to win support for the fight against a killing or disabling disease, as can be seen from the generous public support for so many disease-focused medical research charities. With rare exceptions saving lives is ethically – if not always technically – easy. You can do it again and again. Yesteryear's Newcastle miner, spared by Davy's lamp from a suffocating death in a collapsed mine, is saved again by tetanus vaccination, and again by antibiotics. He becomes an old man. To many he is then seen as a burden – chronic lung trouble from long exposure to coal dust, drawing a pension, dependent. Small wonder if he has a problem with self-esteem and suffers a lonely and dispirited old age.

We may have very mixed feelings about growing old ourselves but it is surely time that we took a new look at our changing world and the forces that are shaping it.

The declines in mortality rates of older people are forcing the forecasts of future life expectancy to be revised upwards. Should we be pleased or depressed? Surely we should be pleased, but it is astonishing how poorly this news is sometimes received. Just last summer, an article presenting new forecasts of even longer life spans in the G7 countries was published in one of the world's leading science journals. A brief editorial trailer for this report announced glumly that the situation was 'even worse than expected'. I wonder just how old was the member of the editorial team who penned that piece?

One cannot pretend for a moment that there is not a lot that is disagreeable about getting older. This is all the more reason why we should direct unprecedented attention to ensuring that all reasonable effort be directed at removing the obstacles to enjoyment of the later years of life. This is not mere altruism nor a pat on the back for our older fellow citizens, put, like the old donkey, out to grass. First and foremost it is a recognition of that most fundamental of human rights, respect for all individuals as equals. It is absolutely staggering not only how much prejudice exists against age but also how unaware of it we remain. On a regular basis we read, hear or ourselves make flippant, jokey or negative remarks about the state of being old. 'Grumpy old', 'silly old', 'boring old', 'dirty old' – the linkages are so familiar that we fail to notice what we are doing. If we were suddenly to acquire the same sensitivity to ageism that we have to racism and sexism, we would be in for a shock. But we do not. Do we not realise that we will all grow old? Can we not celebrate the fact that this privilege has been won for us by our collective ingenuity? Do we not realise that the best prospect for our own happiness in old age is to build a world in which equality, independence and active participation of all generations are positively encouraged?

Science has prepared the ground for the longevity revolution and science will take this revolution forward in ways that we cannot yet forecast with certainty. Yet the challenge of ageing and extended longevity is much bigger than a challenge that can be met with one discipline alone. Thus, it is vitally important that we build the interdisciplinary bridges between all of those who must confront the global challenge of ageing. We need to ask the hard questions. Should we rethink the age of retirement? After all, retirement at sixty-five was first introduced when lives were a good deal shorter. How should we weigh the costs of research and treatment for Alzheimer's disease against, say, the costs of research and treatment for infertility? How much should we be prepared to spend on redesigning our housing and transport systems so that older people are not needlessly cut off from active participation in our society? Why not put an internet connection into every home so that old and young alike can benefit from the IT revolution, with all its promise to ease communications of every sort, including new kinds of health care?

New scientific understanding means that we can never think of ageing in the same way again. We are at the end of the old 'old age'. We know that we will all die one day, but this day is being pushed back further and further. Our longer lives are carrying us into new territory for which we need to plan and prepare ourselves. We cannot afford complacency. If we ignore the implications of the longevity revolution and fail to plan for the radically different world that will soon surround us, crisis will be upon us and our bright dreams of a brave old world will surely fade and die.

2

Thread of Life

Delivered at the Cold Spring Harbor Laboratory, New York

We sometimes say, *in extremis*, that a person's life hangs by a thread. In fact, all our lives hang by a thread all the time. The thread in question is DNA, the medium through which we inherit our genetic destiny. DNA directs our growth and all of the vital processes on which we depend for survival. DNA is the thread of life, but is it also the thread of death? Does DNA control our end as it controls our beginning? In my first lecture, I described the revolution in human longevity that has taken place over the last few generations. Today, I shall look at the companion revolution in the life sciences – a revolution that has unfolded with breathtaking speed over the last half

19

century and which has accelerated greatly of late. It is this revolution that will allow us to understand the role of DNA in the ageing process.

When the first draft of the human genome was announced on 26 June 2000, the world's press rejoiced in the prospect of continuing, even accelerating, the postponement of death that had been the great success story of the twentieth century. This enthusiasm was reflected in reports of a telephone call between President Clinton and Prime Minister Blair, in which the president congratulated the prime minister that his baby son Leo had, at a stroke, gained twenty-five years in life expectancy. Politicians' promises are not always the best arbiters of future reality, but the personal nature of the president's message suggests he was sincere. Was he right? And what are we to make of claims that even longer life spans are just around the corner?

DNA plays a dual role in our lives. Like Theseus of old, it combines power and vulnerability – it is both master and servant of fate. On the one hand, DNA is the medium in which our genetic endowment is written. It is the information coded in our personal DNA sequence which we can probe for the presence or absence of particular gene variants – or polymorphisms – that might affect our future. Seen in this light, DNA plays a fixed role in each of our lives. Our interest is in the differences between one person's DNA and another's and in what these tell us about biological individuality. But our personal DNA is by no means as constant as we might wish. DNA is a working molecule to which our cells refer continually. It is not some dusty tome tucked away in the reference section of the cell but a hive of activity, more akin to a busy internet web site. Just like a web site, it experiences a continual stream of hits. Most of these hits are harmless requests for data, involving simply a readout of a genetic string of As, Cs, Gs and Ts, like the bit strings of zeros and ones that are downloaded from web sites. But some are real hits by agents of damage which result in lasting harm. It is these latter hits that cause the information coded in our DNA to become corrupted with the passage of time, and it may be these hits that cause us to age.

If we look first at the vulnerable side of DNA, the bad news, I am afraid, is that even as I speak your DNA is in trouble. As I spoke the last sentence, the DNA in your body experienced literally billions of damaging hits. The attack rate on DNA has been estimated at 10,000 damaging hits per cell per day. Your body comprises about one hundred thousand billion cells, so the carnage is considerable. Lest you worry unduly, let me assure you at once that even as each hit lands, your cellular emergency services are on the lookout for trouble and putting it right. But, good as these systems are, they are not perfect and some of the damage will persist. During the lecture tonight you will use up one ten-thousandth part of 1 per cent of your life expectancy. It is not a lot, and you will not feel it, but another grain of sand will have passed through the hourglass of your life.

The villain that is doing most of this damage to your DNA is oxygen. We tend to think of oxygen as friend rather than foe, but it is dangerous stuff. When I light my fire on a cold winter evening, it is the chemical reaction of oxygen with carbon that makes the coals glow hot. But if a spark were to escape from the fire, the same oxygen might burn the house down. Inside the cells of our bodies thousands of minute structures called mitochondria use oxygen to produce energy, and the same oxygen also produces a kind of spark. The inside of the cell is wet, of course, so the burning is, in reality, a damp kind of chemistry, but the sparks, called 'free radicals', are no less destructive for being surrounded by water. Free radicals damage whatever they touch, including our DNA. We have growing reason to believe that it is the oxidative damage caused by free radicals which plays an important role in ageing.

Not all of the damage to DNA is caused by oxygen, of course. There are other factors that regularly damage DNA, like sunlight or tobacco smoke. Nor is DNA the only target for free radicals – our membranes and proteins get hit too. But hits to our DNA are liable to have a lasting effect, because the occasional hit that fails to get repaired correctly can lead to a permanent alteration in the DNA sequence. In this respect, the very zeal with which the DNA repair systems guard against change can be our undoing, since once the sequence is changed, it is the new but erroneous sequence that becomes the object of protection. When I was a child, the game of Chinese whispers was popular at parties. I expect you know it. The first player makes up a story and whispers it into the second player's ear. The second player whispers it in the third player's ear, and so on. By the time the message has gone around, the original tale of how Lucy's cat got shut in the coal shed might well be an account of a blue hat that got stuck on a goat's head. DNA plays its own version of Chinese whispers all the time. It is quite possible that there is no longer a single cell in your body that has exactly the same DNA sequence as that which was in you when you began your life as a fertilised egg.

Thus goes the story of vulnerability − of how the slings and arrows of outrageous fortune beat relentlessly at our DNA. But DNA is also master of its destiny. A few moments ago I assured you that most of the DNA damage currently causing mayhem in your cells will be put right. It will be put right because encoded in your genome are instructions for extremely sophisticated DNA repair. You might reasonably ask why, if your DNA is so smart, it does not keep you going for ever. The humbling answer is, it just can't be bothered.

As we saw in my previous lecture, our evolutionary ancestors lived at a time when life was typically brutish and short. In such circumstances, the body was likely to die soon from an accidental cause, rendering any idea of potential immortality somewhat hypothetical. Maintenance does not come cheap and reproduction was more important, so your DNA, in its role as master of your fate, skimped on the maintenance and treated your body as disposable. It is galling to think that we age because our ancestral genes attached limited importance to our individual survival, but we can at least take comfort from the fact that we live a good deal longer than most of our companion species on this planet. Those of us who keep pets soon grow used to a succession of hamsters, budgies, cats or dogs in our lives. It is only the giant tortoises in our zoos that get the chance to feel the same way about their keepers.

The disparity in the life spans of species is scientifically very valuable, for we can test ideas about genetic factors that control the rate of ageing by comparing species that age fast with species that age more slowly. Pioneering work in the mid-1970s found that cells from long-lived species are better at DNA repair than cells from short-lived animals. It has since been confirmed in many laboratories, including my own, that cells from the long-lived animals are generally better at maintaining and protecting themselves. During the last decade we have seen exciting work being done with simple organisms such as fruitflies and roundworms, which has shown that long-lived mutants in these species generally gain their extended longevity from genetic alterations that increase the capacity to resist or repair damage. It is attractive to think that what a mutant roundworm can do, we might be able to do for ourselves. But before we let our imaginations run away with the possibilities of boundless extension of life, it is worth thinking about just how we might go about it. One place to start will be by trying to identify the genetic determinants of human longevity from among the vast array of data now emerging from the human genome project.

There are strong indications that a search for genetic determinants of human longevity will not be fruitless. We have convincing evidence that life expectancy can be inherited. Since biblical times it has been believed that the best recipe for a long life is to choose your parents well, and it has been reassuring to discover that the old adage has more than a grain of truth. Twin research – that favourite tool of the human geneticist – has shown that monozygotic twins, with all of their genes in common, have life spans that are more similar than those of dizygotic twins, who share just 50 per cent of their genes. Other kinds of study, including a recent report based on analysis of the entire population of Iceland, have come to similar conclusions. But these studies also reveal that life span is not inherited in as clear-cut a manner as blood groups or the colours of Gregor Mendel's famous peas. The genetic studies show that the inheritance of human life span is not that strong. It appears that our genes account for about a quarter of what determines the lengths of our lives.

There is a common misconception that as soon as we begin to trawl the gene pool for genes that affect the ageing process, we will fish out genes for ageing, genes for Alzheimer's disease, genes for osteoarthritis, and so on. The reality is that we are most unlikely to discover genes *for* any of these traits. The idea that there exist genes for ageing was knocked on the head half a century ago by the Nobel laureate Peter Medawar, but it is taking a long time to die. Or rather, like Count Dracula, it keeps rising from the dead. The reality is that the vast majority of wild animals die young. Therefore, there is neither a need to evolve genes for ageing, for example to control population size, nor an opportunity to do so. Far from evolving genes for ageing, animals evolved genes for longevity. As animals became better adapted to their environments and thus able to avoid some of the dangers therein, it became worthwhile to invest in things like better DNA repair. Once we recognise that the genes we must seek are genes for longevity, not ageing, our task becomes more realistic but at the same time more complicated. We can expect tens, or even hundreds, of genes to be involved in the networks of maintenance systems that keep us alive. Working them out is going to require the very newest gene technologies and some highly sophisticated computation.

What is true for ageing is also true for the diseases of

later life. It makes no sense to think in terms of genes for Alzheimer's disease, except in rare families where particular mutations produce unusually early onset. Even in these cases, the genes which are mutated probably do not *cause* the disease but merely accelerate its progression. To understand the real, underlying causes of conditions like Alzheimer's and osteoarthritis we must probe for the weak links in gene networks that probably evolved to do us good and not harm. We can expect to find that many of the genes that contribute to such conditions are not all bad, but rather are genes that at an earlier stage in life do us good. Whether a gene is good or bad depends on the circumstances. This is strikingly illustrated by the gene that codes for the sickle-cell variant of haemoglobin. In malarial West Africa, the sickle-cell gene conferred protection against fever on those who inherited just one copy, but at the cost of imposing a crippling blood disorder on those who inherited two. In circumstances where the risk of infection with malaria was high, the scales of natural selection were tipped in favour of maintaining a relatively high frequency of the sickle-cell gene within the population. But times change and people of West African origin who live now in non-malarial regions run the risk of sickle-cell disease as an unfortunate cruel legacy of past evolutionary advantage. Much the same may be true of genes which predispose us to late-life diseases. A prime example can be found if we turn our attention to the very tips of the thread of life. One of the processes that we believe may have a role to play in ageing is the gradual loss of DNA sequence from the ends of our chromosomes – our telomeres – as cells divide. We know in principle how to arrest this decline by the throw of a genetic switch, but we also know that throwing this particular switch is one of the things that a deranged cell does when it becomes malignant. There is a growing belief among those who study cellular ageing that the gradual loss of DNA from our telomeres – and whatever this may do to age us – is a price that our genome agreed to pay in order to protect us better from cancer. In past times, when life expectancy was short we reaped the benefits without paying the price. In the future, we may have to choose. But before we can make an informed choice we need to discover the rules of the game.

I said at the beginning of this lecture that there are two sides to the character of DNA – its power and its vulnerability. We have seen something of the vulnerability of DNA – its susceptibility to damage – and we have seen something of its power – how genetic factors influence the lengths of our lives, albeit in complex fashion. But, as the Greek storytellers knew full well, a key ingredient of any tale is the *interplay* between the strengths and weaknesses of its hero.

It is clear that an important facet of the genetics of ageing is the interaction between DNA damage and the genetic control of DNA repair. Nowhere is this more starkly illustrated than in the rare genetic disorder known as Werner's syndrome, where mutation in a gene that controls a part of the DNA repair machinery leads to a two-fold acceleration of many features of the ageing process and a drastic shortening of life span. The cells in a person with Werner's syndrome show abnormally heavy burdens of DNA damage. But the vulnerability of the genetic message in all of us extends beyond mere damage to the DNA sequence. Not only are there errors in how DNA is copied and repaired, but there are all kinds of hiccups and random variations in how the genetic instructions are translated into proteins, in how proteins are transported around the cell, in how genes get turned on and off, in how cells interpret signals from other cells, and so on. The system works because evolutionary pressure has ensured that the ensuing muddle is well enough contained that it does not interfere with our vital functions during the all-important early years. This is what mattered in our ancestral past. But variations that do not affect us until middle and later life are relatively unconstrained. As we look deeper, we find that our genetic blueprint is not so deterministic after all. Genes do not specify the end of our lives with any precision. They do not shepherd us towards some pre-ordained goal like the guidance system of a cruise missile. They merely point us in a certain direction and do their best to keep us ticking along until muddle gains the upper hand. What determines where we each end up is a three-fold blend of nature, nurture and chance.

In these heady days of revolutionary fervour, it is perhaps natural that our imaginations should run wild with the new possibilities unfolding before us. Designer babies with the brains of Einstein, the looks of Brigitte Bardot, and the longevity of Methuselah? I well remember the excitement that swept Europe's young people in May 1968 when a spirit of change, prompted by the events in Paris, was in the air. But the hard realities of life have a nasty habit of reasserting themselves, and I was struck that among the excited talk that accompanied last summer's genome headlines there was almost no serious consideration of just how the science would actually deliver the fabulously extended life spans that were suggested. Such extrapolations from current research as were on offer had more the flavour of science fiction. To be sure, we can extend the life span of a roundworm or a fruitfly, and we can learn lessons that will surely tell us something about human ageing. It is a very far cry, however, from modifying the life of a fly or worm to altering the life span of a human being. We can conceive, in principle, of gene therapy that could alter human ageing. But as yet we neither have a clear picture of the genes we would wish to change, nor know if changing them would do more harm than good. Nor have we cracked the much simpler problem of delivering effective gene therapy for single gene disorders such as cystic fibrosis. In the case of cystic fibrosis, we have known for some time exactly what we would like to be able to do. Would that we could do it. President Nixon's 1960s war on cancer saw billions poured into cancer research, yet we suffer cancer still.

I am excited about ageing research. I have made it my life's work. I welcome with open arms the revolution that will take us forward with greater force. But I see two very real dangers in the exaggeration of expectations for human longevity from genome research. Firstly, although the potential of such research is enormous, it is simply foolish and potentially damaging to expect too much too soon. Bubbles have a nasty habit of bursting, as the stock market over-valuation of dotcom businesses has shown. We have learned – not easily, and with many a false hope raised – to temper our impatience for radical breakthroughs in cancer therapy with more realistic expectations. We should do the same for ageing. Secondly, if we pander too readily to what is often little more than a restatement of the ancient fantasy of an elixir of youth, we distract attention from the more realistic and immediate priorities of ageing research – the improvement of quality of the later years of life. We run the risk of marginalising and trivialising the concerns of those who are in the front line of a battle from which we would rather run away. I believe that the insights from human genome research will tell us how the machinery of human ageing works, not immediately how to drive it. This, however, will be no small gain. We might reasonably anticipate that a deeper understanding of how the normal ageing process feeds into such age-related diseases as Alzheimer's, osteoporosis and macular degeneration will expose an array of new approaches to intervene and postpone these and other unwelcome conditions.

President Clinton promised Leo Blair an extra twenty-five years of life. Given the time that it takes to translate groundbreaking new research into effective application, it's a tough challenge for science. Penicillin was first discovered by Fleming in 1928 and took nearly twenty years to pass into general use. The discoveries we need to make to extend human life span are more complex and will inevitably take longer to assess. To demonstrate efficacy of a treatment that can extend a life that is already long, or delay a disease that develops over many years, is not something that can be done in a hurry, particularly since the most effective interventions are likely to be those that commence early. Nevertheless, President Clinton might just be right. Science is on track to discover the deep secrets of ageing.

3

Sex and Death

Delivered at the Royal Museum, Edinburgh

The greatest physical asset of any of us, even those as well endowed in other respects as Dolly Parton or Arnold Schwarzenegger, is the soft grey hemisphere that sits between our ears. The human brain is a masterpiece of evolution but it complicates our lives, and nowhere is this more apparent than when we struggle with the big questions of sex and death. It could be said that the trouble started with Aristotle, who believed that each sex act had a direct life-shortening effect. I shudder to think of the unhappiness that wise old Greek must have caused when we see, many centuries later, this troubling idea surfacing in the work of the metaphysical poets. It would be hard to find gloomier expression than John Donne's mournful musing: 'Since each such act, they say, diminisheth the length of life a day ... I'll no more dote and run to pursue things which hath endamaged me'.

Now if you were to ask the male praying mantis being eaten by his bride during the act of copulation whether the metaphysical poets were correct that the orgasm is 'a little death', he would probably agree. He might even drop the word 'little'. You might get the same answer from the Pacific salmon, which spawns but once and then dies. But is it true of you and me? Does sex shorten our lives? Can it be, as some have suggested, that ageing and death are the price we pay for sex? Does it make sense to think in terms of a 'reproductive duty' to the species, leaving us surplus to requirement when duty is done? And what, if these worrying notions are true, are we to make of the post-menopausal woman? These are the questions I shall examine in today's lecture, and I shall hope to show you not only that the answers are reassuring (on the whole), but also that they tell us a great deal about the biological background to our revolution in longevity.

In fact, Aristotle was right; there is a relationship between sex and death, but it is more interesting than even Aristotle suspected. The catalytic insight came in 1881 from the distinguished German naturalist August Weismann. What Weismann realised was that in a multicellular body like yours or mine, there is a profound division of labour between two principal kinds of cells. On the one hand, there is the germ-line – the egg- or sperm-forming cells of the ovary or testis. These are the cells that, if we have children, transmit our genes into the next generation. The rest of the cells – those making up the other organs of the body – Weismann termed the soma.

In the early stages of life on planet earth, before the distinction between germ-line and somatic cells evolved, the responsibility for generating new individuals was shared by every cell. Indeed, most organisms were probably unicellular and their descendants are with us today – bacteria, amoebae and the like. But as cells came to live in clumps of genetically identical clones, the separation of germ-line and soma offered wonderful new possibilities for some of the cells, freed from the need to support procreation, to become specialists. In our bodies today we find red blood cells, specialised for transporting oxygen and other constituents around the body. We find white blood cells, designed to police the body for intruders and destroy them. We find brain and nerve cells, engineered for the conduction of electrical signals. We find the cells of the lens of the eye, uniquely translucent in order to transmit and focus light upon the retina. It would be hard to imagine how such diverse specialisms could be supported if each of these cells needed also to retain the capacity to produce a new baby.

The distinction between germ-line and soma enabled such extraordinary advances in the evolution of the higher forms of life that we might almost forgive the terrible price we have paid. For it was this, not sex, that caused us to age and die. There are species that age and don't have sex, like parthenogenetic whiptail lizards, and there are species that have sex and don't age, like the freshwater hydra. But although hydra are capable of sex, they often don't bother and make do instead with vegetative reproduction, by budding. Almost any part of a hydra can generate a new individual. Its germ-line permeates its body and it has no real soma to speak of. It is this lack of distinction between germ-line and soma that allows hydra to evade the ageing process. The presence or absence of ageing is always associated, as far as we know, with the presence or absence of the soma/germ-line distinction.

To understand why the soma/germ-line distinction is so important for ageing, we should first observe that the germ-line simply cannot be allowed to fail in its duty of keeping going indefinitely. If it did – if, for example, it permitted cumulative damage to build up in its DNA sequence – it would rapidly become extinct. Some change to the DNA sequence must of course occur, since otherwise evolution would be stalled, but the kind of damage that builds up in the somatic cells of our bodies during our lifetime would be intolerable if it were to occur to a similar extent in the germ-line. This immortality of the germ-line is not a theoretical concept. It is as real as life itself. Each of us could, if the records were available, trace our ancestry back to the very earliest cellular forms of life on earth. Throughout the billions of years of evolutionary history, an unbroken chain of cell divisions has made us what we are today.

When we consider the soma, however, we find that there is no corresponding requirement for somatic cells to keep their DNA in good shape indefinitely. We have nothing of either parent's soma in us, and there is nothing of our soma in our children. It just does not matter, biologically speaking, if our somatic cells eventually fall apart. The somatic cells comprise the individual and that – important as it may be to you and me – is all that they will ever be required to do.

Life in the natural world is brutish and short. All that the organism needs from its somatic cells is that they can keep the soma in good enough shape until an age when the likelihood of still being alive is negligible. When we factor in the consideration that maintenance and repair of somatic cells does not come cheap, it makes sense to trim back the maintenance of the somatic cells and divert the energy thereby saved into helping with the all-important business of reproduction. The result was that the soma became disposable, and with that came ageing. It was in 1977 that this realisation came to me – a Eureka! moment that happened, appropriately enough, as I took my bath. At the time, the idea was highly controversial because the prevailing view then was that ageing is programmed. But in the years since, the evidence in support of the disposable soma theory – as the idea is called – has become strong. It is this idea that teaches us to understand that the primary cause of ageing is the gradual build-up of faults in the cells and organs of the body.

It is always exceptions that prove the rule, and being here in Edinburgh I should be remiss if I did not mention Dolly the sheep and the remarkable feat of somatic cell cloning. At the time this breakthrough was announced I was in Budapest, as a Visiting Fellow at the Institute for Advanced Study. I don't think I shall ever forget the glee with which my host's secretary announced that not only were men's somas disposable, but their germ-lines were redundant too. Like many a scientist, I was amazed at the Roslin Institute's success in transferring the nucleus from an adult somatic cell into an enucleated egg and producing a viable animal. What Dolly and other cloning successes have shown is that in at least some somatic cells, the integrity of the DNA may be relatively spared. On the other hand, it was found with Dolly that the successful nuclear transfer was one among a considerable number of failures. Being random, the cellular damage that leads to the ageing of somatic tissues is by no means a uniform affair.

If the disposable soma theory is correct and ageing

results from a trade-off between reproduction and maintenance, then Aristotle might have been right that romantic ardour has a life-shortening effect. And if Aristotle had been a fruitfly, he would have been spot on. Linda Partridge and her colleagues have shown that a life of chastity works wonders for would-be fruitfly centenarians and that the cost of egg-laying has a delayed harmful effect on female survival, probably because the making of all those eggs siphons away energy that might otherwise be used for survival. But in humans there is no evidence that sexual activity shortens life – indeed, quite the reverse has been suggested. Nor is there any strong indication that having children grinds you down in the longevity sense, however contrary to parents' experience this may seem. But there is some evidence that there is a trade-off between our genetic predisposition to long life and to fertility.

Studying human biology is complicated because, as we all know, there is a great deal that is not strictly biological which influences our lives. On the other hand, we have astonishingly detailed records, including details of births, deaths and marriages, which have accumulated over many years. So it was to this rich resource that I turned, together with Rudi Westendorp, an epidemiologist from the University of Leiden, in order to ask whether there might be buried evidence of a trade-off between human fertility and longevity. The records we used had been compiled on a commercially available genealogical database, containing records of British aristocrats going back to the eighth century. The database contained records for 33,497 individuals. We chose to study aristocrats firstly because their records have been better preserved, and secondly because aristocrats enjoyed the best living conditions which, in earlier times, would have given them the best chances of living a long life. There are many ways in which poverty adversely affects both fertility and survival, and these might have masked the patterns we were looking for.

What we found was very curious. There was, of course, a trend over time towards increasing life spans and smaller family sizes. As others had observed before, these trends among the aristocracy were about 150 years ahead of the general population, confirming the privileged status of aristocrats as a group. After making allowance for these underlying trends, we discovered that the longest-lived aristocrats tended, on the average, to have the greatest trouble with fertility. So, taking the pattern as a whole, it does appear that a predisposition to above-average longevity may be linked to below-average fertility.

Perhaps the oddest thing about human reproduction, something that sets us apart from the rest of the animal kingdom, is the menopause. The mystery of menopause is this: why should women invariably lose their fertility when they are far short of showing advanced signs of biological ageing, and when it happens neither to monkeys nor to men? To be sure, there is talk of a male menopause, or andropause. But neither in men nor in female apes is there a *universal* loss of fertility at such a relatively early age. Male reproductive ageing is variable. Some men may experience early loss of reproductive functions. Others retain fertility and may indeed father children at a great old age. There is no such spectrum of possibilities for women. Menopause shuts the door to motherhood with blunt finality at around the age of fifty. Fertility declines in advance of this for five to ten years.

Reproduction is so important for Darwinian fitness that anything which impedes fertility should make us ponder the evolutionary stakes that may be at play. Menopause is a unique feature of the human female life history and its explanation is most likely to be found among the other elements that distinguish human evolution from our companion species on this planet. Just last month, my colleague Daryl Shanley and I published an evolutionary analysis that throws new light on the factors which may be responsible.

During the evolution of our hominid ancestors, two unprecedented developments took place. Firstly, the human brain underwent extraordinarily rapid growth. Secondly, we acquired the capacity for a level of advanced social and cultural interaction not previously seen. In concert with these developments, we evolved increased life spans, presumably because of new evolutionary pressure to make the soma a bit less disposable.

After all, there is little point in evolving a big brain and using it make your life safer if your DNA falls apart before you have been able to reap the benefits of these advances. Such a process might happily continue – brains getting bigger and lives getter longer – but for one worrisome snag. The baby's brain still needs to pass through the mother's pelvis at the time of birth. Worse still, the physical dimensions of the pelvis are tightly constrained by the mechanics of the increasingly upright human gait.

Natural selection is a master of compromise. While a design engineer might suggest that the birth canal be rerouted, perhaps via the abdomen, such radical redesign rarely occurs. What happened instead was that babies came to be born with their brains half grown. Compared to other placental mammals, the human infant is unusually incomplete at birth. A lamb, calf or foal walks with its mother within hours of its birth. A human baby takes more than a year to accomplish this feat. On the other hand, in order not to extend the period of such high dependency even longer, birth is delayed until the baby's brain is as big as possible. The result is that humans have unusually difficult deliveries, which increases the dangers if things go wrong. The dangers are tragically clear from the high levels of maternal mortality that occurred – and still occur in the developing countries – in the absence of modern obstetric care.

So there we were, the pinnacle of evolution, but reproductively speaking in a fine old mess. Social and cultural evolution was occurring fast, and life expectancy was growing rapidly. For perhaps the first time in our evolutionary history, significant numbers of women began surviving to an age when the signs of senescence were starting to be felt. Initially, it may have been only a small number surviving past fifty, but it brought a new challenge. If females retained fertility indefinitely, and if those who survived to older ages continued to become pregnant, the already difficult business of giving birth would become downright dangerous. There is some truth, at least in natural circumstances, in the idea that the fifty-year-old body is too old to give birth properly.

The solution, as you might have guessed, was to limit fertility to ages when it was relatively safe, even though this meant forgoing the genetic advantages of having as many children as possible. However, there were compensatory benefits. Firstly, the older mother would be spared the risks of a late pregnancy and her dependent children would be protected from becoming orphans. Secondly, with an increasing tendency for living in extended kin groups, the post-reproductive female could assist her daughters with their reproduction, perhaps by relieving them of some of the burdens of providing for their dependent offspring. There is good evidence from hunter-gatherer societies, particularly the Hadza of East Africa, that the fulfilment of such a role by grandmothers enhances the child-raising capacity of their daughters and decreases the mortality of grandchildren. An important concept in evolutionary biology, developed by the late Bill Hamilton, is the idea of 'inclusive fitness' – that one's genetic contribution to future generations should be measured in terms of the survival and reproductive success of kin other than just one's immediate offspring. What Daryl Shanley and I showed in our paper, is that it requires all of these factors to be bundled together before it becomes clear that the menopause serves a genuine evolutionary advantage. It is this stringent requirement that explains the uniqueness of the human menopause and it tells us that post-menopausal women, far from being, in Darwinian terms, worn-out biological has-beens, are actually very special.

If it is correct that the menopause represents a distinct evolutionary advantage, as I believe to be the case, this was a hugely significant step. For probably the first time ever, an adaptation arose that specifically reflected the new value of older organisms. After aeons of largely neglecting the fate of the disposable soma, natural selection finally woke up to the fact that older women were so valuable that late fertility became dispensable instead.

As we celebrate the longevity revolution and look to the future, it helps to understand where we come from and where we may be headed. The evolutionary insights that throw light on the relationship between sex and death are an important part of explaining why and how we age. They may also help us understand the directions in which the forces of natural selection, slow but resolute as a glacier, may be directing us. The circumstances under which we now procreate and die are very different from those which shaped our present-day life-history. It will be interesting to ask where natural selection may steer our descendants, even if we are not around to see.

Finally, no discussion of sex and death would be complete without visiting the intriguing question of why it is that women live longer than men. The fact that having a Y-chromosome instead of a second X-chromosome shortens life by almost 10 per cent is one of life's oddities, made all the stranger by the fact that among birds the chromosomal determination of sex works the other way around, yet still it is the females that live longer. There is, as yet, no completely satisfactory answer why things should be so, but I believe that the existence of a female menopause and the absence of a male menopause offers a clue.

Males and females make an equal genetic contribution to their offspring, but females make a more direct physiological contribution to their young, by nurturing the foetus in the womb and by suckling the young in the case of a mammal, or by forming and provisioning the egg in the case of egg-laying species like birds, reptiles, insects and amphibians. There is therefore a sense in which the state of the female soma makes an important contribution to the success of her reproduction, and the female soma may therefore be less disposable than the male. The difference appears to be enough, in humans, to tip the balance between evolving menopause or not. As for the mechanisms through which the difference is produced, the sex hormones appear the likely culprits. High testosterone levels are associated with risk-taking and aggression in younger males, and with heart disease and prostate cancer in later life. Castration in males, as judged from data on domesticated animals, appears at least partially to equalise male and female longevity. Aristotle, with his views on the life-shortening effects of sex and his pioneering philosophical quest for truth, just might have agreed to try the experiment. But I am not so sure.

4

Making Choices

Delivered at the Berryhill Retirement Village, Stoke-on-Trent

The freedom to make – and continue making – choices is perhaps the greatest single index of well-being. Choice matters in ageing for two very powerful reasons. First, although many fruits of the scientific revolution lie in the future, scientific understanding of the ageing process already tells us that there is a great deal that we can do right now by making the right choices. Second, as we get older, choice often seems to be taken away. The infirmity of age undoubtedly sets barriers to certain kinds of choice, while financial hardship – an all-too-common companion of old age – sets others. But choice tends to be limited by age much more than is really necessary, through either negative expectations or just poor planning. The revolution in longevity puts choice high on the list of priorities.

It is because choice is so important that I chose to give today's lecture, on the subject 'Making choices', here at Berryhill retirement village, near Stoke-on-Trent. Berryhill takes for granted that members of its community have the right to choose. We all know what can happen in institutions where choice is suppressed for the sake of so-called efficiency. But if choice leads to health, and health leads to reduced dependency, then choice is more efficient, not less. When scientists began to study the rhythms of the heart, they made a surprising discovery. The healthy heart has a *chaotic* rhythm – chaotic, that is, in the mathematical sense. Within certain limits, the heart's rhythm bounces all over the place, and it bounces back. The sick heart, on the other hand, settles to the same dogged pattern. It has lost the dynamic range of health. Berryhill is not chaotic, but it certainly does a great deal to preserve the dynamic range of health.

In an earlier lecture I said that about a quarter of what determines the length of our lives is inherited through the genes. This means that three-quarters is determined not by our genes but by something else. This 'something else' includes the choices we make about how we treat our bodies through life. These choices can have big effects on how we will age.

If we look around the world, we find that even

among the developed nations there are significant variations in life expectancy. Japan, for example, has the longest life spans. It also has exceptionally low levels of heart disease. In the United Kingdom or the USA, the death rate from heart disease among sixty-five to seventy-four-year-olds is about 600 deaths per 100,000 people each year. In Japan, the number is less than 100 – an astonishing six times lower. But if we look at Japanese people who have migrated to the United States, we find that Japanese Americans typically have the American rather than the Japanese patterns of disease and mortality. The switch occurs when they alter their choices and, for better or worse, adopt the American way of life.

To understand why lifestyle has such a great impact, we should recall that ageing is not some fixed process but comes about through the accumulation of subtle faults within the cells and organs of our bodies as we live our lives. For this reason, the ageing process is malleable. It can be altered by choices that affect either our exposure to damage or our ability to cope with it. Just as we alter the life span of a car by how well, or badly, we drive and maintain it, we alter the ageing of our body by how well, or badly, we take care of it. We are not programmed to die, but to survive. There is much we can do to assist this programming as it strives to help us.

The obvious starting point is nutrition. In a very

literal sense, we are what we eat. The material that forms the flesh and bones of our bodies is material that we have consumed. If we eat foods that harm us, we add to the burden of damage. Conversely, if we eat foods that play a part in our maintenance and repair systems, we enhance our body's capacity to keep damage at bay. The idea that we should eat healthily is hardly new. But what is new is that we now have an understanding of precisely why certain foods are beneficial for ageing, while others are not. We can translate traditional health education, founded as it was on good old common sense, into choices that are evidence-based.

The human body, unlike the car, does a great deal to maintain itself. Many of the materials that the body requires for its maintenance can be synthesised within our cells, but some must come from outside. Trace elements such as zinc and selenium are required only in tiny quantities but they play essential roles in the chemistry of life. Our health suffers if they are absent. Vitamin C is something else that we must get through our foods. Some species manufacture their own vitamin C but humans cannot. We get our vitamin C from fruits and vegetables. It is an important antioxidant. When a molecule of vitamin C meets a free radical, it becomes oxidised, thereby rendering the free radical harmless. The body can recycle the vitamin C so it can do this time and again, but it cannot make the vitamin C in the first place.

Growing awareness of the role played by vitamins and trace elements in health has led to a burgeoning market in nutritional supplements, many of which are sold on the basis of their alleged anti-ageing properties. You can emerge from a shop carrying a bag full of all kinds of pills and potions that, if the labels could be believed, would have you living as long as Methuselah.

It is, in fact, extremely hard to confirm the efficacy of nutritional supplements. Those who take them are neither a representative nor homogeneous group. Some are health conscious to an extreme and do a great deal else to maintain high levels of personal health. Others lead terrible lifestyles and clutch at supplements as at straws, to rescue their bodies from the consequences of neglect. The only reliable way to assess the efficacy of a nutritional supplement is to conduct a double-blind trial, where neither the researcher nor the volunteer knows until the study is complete whether they are getting the real thing or a placebo. As yet, there have been remarkably few studies of this kind on the effects of nutritional supplements on the ageing process, and those which have been done tell ambivalent tales.

Our best evidence that nutrition has important effects on ageing comes from epidemiological studies where the patterns of nutrition are studied in populations, and statistical associations with health and disease are detected. The long lives of the Japanese are attributed to their traditional diet, which is rich in fish, vegetables, and soya products, while being low in sugar and fats. The Mediterranean diet, also associated with longer life, is rich in vegetables, fish and olive oil. Wine, another standard ingredient of the Mediterranean diet, is happily also good for health – at least in moderation. The death rates from heart disease in Mediterranean countries are a good deal lower than those in northern Europe, even if they are not as spectacularly low as in Japan. Italy, for example, has a three-fold lower rate than the UK.

Much research is now being done to identify exactly how and why the nutritional choices we make have these long-term impacts on health and longevity. Ageing results from accumulation of damage. If we remove known sources of damage from our consumption we slow the damaging process. Smoking damages us. Toxins damage us. Saturated fats damage us. Excess sugar damages us. We are beginning to discover much about the biochemistry of these different kinds of damage and how they play their part in age-related degeneration and disease. On the other hand, if we consume foods that aid the fight against damage – anti-oxidant rich fruits and vegetables and cholesterol-lowering fish and olive oils – we enhance our protection. By narrowing the gap between the rates of damage and repair we can expect to extend our span of healthy life. We know enough already about the underlying processes of ageing to see why that 'nasty green stuff' we tried so hard to avoid as children is truly good for us, while those enticing chips, cakes and sweets are bad.

Another important area of choice is exercise. Our organs were designed to be used and their evolution took place in conditions far removed from today's. It is very striking that the age-related increase in blood pressure, which is almost universal in developed countries, is not seen in people like the Masai of East Africa who maintain very high levels of physical activity throughout life. Sedentary life styles are unnatural and we adopt them at our peril. Not only is exercise good for heart and lung function, it is also essential for healthy bones. Our skeletons are not static but undergo continual remodelling by cells evolved for this purpose. Osteoclasts nibble away at the bone surface, removing microscopic signs of wear and tear. Osteoblasts repair and fill the holes with new bone material. The thing that stimulates these cells to do their work is exercise, which can be as simple as going for a walk or climbing the stairs. It is striking that the rate of hip fracture among older people has increased two-fold during the last fifty years. Changing patterns of exercise may be partly to blame.

We know that exercise is good in youth but we are less aware that it takes on a greater, rather than a lesser significance, as we grow old. A simple task, like rising from a chair, taxes our muscles to a much greater fraction of their residual capacity when we are old than when we are young. Like an athlete, an old person must regularly perform at the limit of his or her physical ability. So however old we are, we can benefit from training, even if we have to perform our exercises from a chair. Randomised controlled trials on the effectiveness of exercise have shown that for older people the increase in muscle strength can be the equivalent of taking the muscle back in time to an age that is fifteen years younger.

In addition to its training effects, there is evidence that exercise can retard – or even reverse – some of the molecular deterioration that accumulates with age. Research in Newcastle, home of the Great North Run, has shown that veteran athletes have fewer mutations in the mitochondria – the cellular power units – of their muscles than non-athletes of similar ages. A key feature of mitochondria is that these tiny organelles have their own small genomes and their own life cycle inside our cells. Long ago, mitochondria were free-living bacteria that found life more comfortable inside another cell and have earned their keep ever since by being useful converters of energy. Each cell contains hundreds or thousands of them and they are forever renewing themselves, even if the cell in which they live has ceased its division. Mixed in among the good mitochondria are mutants that have had their DNA damaged by free radicals. One of the hot research questions in the field of cellular ageing today – one on which my colleagues and I are hard at work – is why the bad mitochondria build up in aged cells like muscle and how this contributes to ageing vulnerability. The benefit of exercise may come about because driving our cells to their energetic limits forces a kind of natural selection among the mitochondria, which helps check the expansion in numbers of the bad ones.

Exercise for the brain is as important as exercise for the body. Memory loss due to age, in the absence of an underlying disease such as Alzheimer's, is much exaggerated. We forget things at all ages, but we are strongly (and wrongly) conditioned to blame only our age if we forget when we are older. Personally I can recall having the equivalent of so-called 'senior moments' since the age of seven, when I sent out invitations to my birthday party but forgot to indicate who they came from.

We must acknowledge, however, that *on the average* certain aspects of cognitive performance do decline with age. I emphasise 'on the average' not only because there are very old individuals whose cognition remains remarkably sharp, but also because regularly practised skills, like music, chess, bridge or crossword puzzles, tend to be unusually well-conserved. Regular mental exercise seems to preserve the patterns of neuronal interconnection that might otherwise atrophy from disuse.

As a gerontologist, I am often asked what I do myself to stave off the ravages of ageing. The answer is that I practise what I preach – at least most of the time. I eat a very varied diet, including a high proportion of non-meat meals. The important thing with healthy eating, as with dieting, is not to attempt the impossible. If you don't enjoy what you eat, it won't work, but experimentation can lead to new tastes being acquired. I used to dislike tofu, but I love it now. I am also passionate about porridge, but that is another story. I do not take nutritional supplements, preferring to get vitamins and trace elements the natural way through foods.

In terms of exercise, I enjoy running but do so irregularly. However, I walk with our dog each morning before breakfast. I keep a bicycle at work to get to meetings in other parts of the university, and I nearly always choose stairs rather than lifts. I am a great believer in the importance of maintaining a positive attitude to life. One is never too old to take up a new challenge or acquire a new skill. My own latest challenge has been to start learning to play the piano, something that brings me enormous pleasure. I have a long list of plans for the future.

I have dealt so far with what we might call the easy choices. I don't want to imply that holding to a healthy diet, sticking with an exercise plan and maintaining a positive attitude through thick and thin is easy. But the choices are, in principle, straightforward. I want now to turn to the harder choices – the choices that our society has to confront as it wakes up to the reality of the longevity revolution. An important question is the priority we place on ensuring that older people are not denied freedoms of choice that younger people take for granted.

Inevitably, ageing involves loss. But prejudice and lack of appropriate provision frequently force a premature closing down of options, sometimes through neglect, sometimes through benign but misguided over-protection. Over-protection can create or reinforce anxiety and self-doubt. If we treat old people as weak-spirited because they are frail, we do them serious injustice. The better alternative is to provide encouragement and support, which boosts confidence and self-reliance, contributing directly to a greater sense of well-being in spite of the infirmities of age. It is this aspect of the Berryhill culture that impressed me most. Berryhill offers its residents the chance to go abseiling or canoeing, even if they must rely for much of their time on a wheelchair. In doing so it breaks the mould in ways that produce benefits far beyond the immediate pleasure of the experience.

Not everyone wants to live in a retirement village and we need a spectrum of choices that reflects the variety of personal preference, which increases rather than decreases with age. We must therefore take a radical look at how society can accommodate its growing numbers of older people while preserving the freedom of choice. New sheltered housing is commonly tucked away on the margins of society, but older people whose mobility is often impaired need to be able to get out and about and engage with the rest of us. Access to amenities like shops, cinemas, parks, banks, museums and even places of work is important. Public transport needs to be reliable and secure.

Immediately, the alarm bells start ringing. How much will it cost? Can we afford it? What about other priorities, like schools? When we talk about hard choices, nearly always we mean that something else will have to be sacrificed to pay for it. Perhaps this is so, and we need very carefully to consider how we balance our priorities. The trouble with our present mechanisms is that we marginalise older people and demean their own sense of self-worth, so that these discussions hardly begin on a level playing field. We tend also to lose sight of the fact that nearly all of us today can expect to grow old. Thus, in adjusting society today to make better provision for today's older generations – the vanguard of the longevity revolution – let us not lose sight of the fact that we are shaping the society in which the current schoolchildren and working generations will themselves grow old. If we decide to invest in creating a better society for older people now, we are not stealing money from the young but investing it for their future as well. Our current short-term fiscal obsessions, coupled with hopelessly prejudiced and outmoded attitudes to ageing, are preventing us from seeing the wood for the trees.

Even from a purely fiscal point of view, it may be a

smart move to invest in better infrastructure for older people if we want to prevent the much-vaunted 'burden' of care from overwhelming us. Properly accounted, the costs of reorganising our society to meet the needs of older people need not be a negative entry on the balance sheet. Interventions such as pacemakers for people with neurocardiovascular instability, a significant cause of falls in old age, have been shown to pay for themselves many times over, when they reduce demand on National Health Service facilities and postpone the age at which the high costs of dependency are incurred. And this is to say nothing of the gain in quality of life. It is all too easy to see how imperfections in our present society lead to dependency. For a variety of reasons, many older people lose the habit of going out. Physical inactivity causes faster wasting of muscle and bone, which leads to increased risk of falls and fractures. Less social interaction also means less mental stimulus, leading to a turning-in on oneself and greater vulnerability to depression.

A stark manifestation of the 'hard choice' mentality is the age-related rationing of medical care. Clearly there is an extremely difficult choice that must be made if there is one kidney available for transplant and ten recipients. But few choices are as tricky as this and we are on thin ice, unsupported by our scientific understanding of the ageing process, if we make general assumptions about health and future life expectancy based solely on age. Age is a statistic that is held to be of paramount importance in a patient's medical notes. But should it be? Is not age used merely as a surrogate for the expected condition of the patient, opening the door to prejudice? Why not get rid of age from the medical record altogether and let the patient's biological state speak for itself?

The revolution in longevity has come so fast that we are still largely stuck in mind-sets of the past. The key ingredient distinguishing ageing from other social divisions is that it affects us all. We need to recognise therefore that when we make choices – sometimes hard financial choices – about initiatives to meet the challenge of an older population, it is not 'them and us' we are dealing with but 'us and us'. We need equitable solutions that will meet our needs at all future stages of our life cycle.

5

New Directions

Delivered at the International Centre for Life,
Newcastle-upon-Tyne

Every revolution has a turning point – a time when the original impetus for change has run its course. History shows that this is often a vulnerable time. Opinion on where to go next is sharply divided. Indecision prevails at precisely the moment when decisive action is most essential. The longevity revolution is no exception. We know where we've come from and why, but we don't have a clear plan of where to go now. Ours has been a revolution *from* – from the terrible waste of life caused by premature death – not a revolution *to*. We are at our turning point now. The decisions we take in the next few years will have far-reaching consequences for the state of future society.

Two hundred years ago most people died before their time. Well, we fixed that. Rarely has a revolution succeeded so well. What we now experience are the deaths associated with old age, with degenerative conditions. Much of modern medicine is concerned with fighting these, pushing back the frontiers of survival further and further. But suddenly we are no longer sure about where we are going and why. Many are the news stories trumpeting that we will soon all live to 130, 200 or 400 years, but what about the *New Yorker* cartoon that showed one old man saying to another: 'I hope I die before science makes me live to 150'?

The ambivalence of our attitudes reflects the confusion of rapid change. Not long ago the attainment of old age was hailed as a success. Ageing today is widely seen as a failure, unless you are as extremely old as Jeanne Calment. I remember being deeply struck by a remark from a former medical colleague whose research was on heart disease: 'There is nothing interesting about the ageing of the cardiovascular system,' he exclaimed, 'it just rots!' What, I wondered, did he feel was the point of his work? What, for that matter, is the point of mine? As a gerontologist, my work addresses how and why we age. But why do it? For me, the answer is clear. The longevity revolution has given us a substantial increase in life expectancy. But the extra years are not as good as we might wish. Conditions like Alzheimer's disease, stroke, osteoporosis and arthritis have a serious effect on quality of life, either by robbing us of our identity or stealing our independence. Our primary goal should be to make headway against these conditions. But how to do it? Is it realistic to think of achieving this goal without altering the ageing process itself?

The idea that science should aim to postpone disabling conditions such as Alzheimer's disease, without necessarily extending life itself, has become something of a mantra. It is a mantra that goes by the name 'compression of morbidity'. The aim is to squeeze the bad things that happen to us at the end of life into as short a period as possible. Another way of putting this is that we want to extend the *health* span, while leaving the life span as it is. On the whole, people seem to find this idea more reassuring than the idea that scientists want to make us all live longer.

The trouble is, however, that compression of morbidity makes assumptions about the extent to which we can decouple ageing and disease. There has long been controversy in medical research circles about whether a condition such as Alzheimer's is strictly a disease, with the implication that we can cure it on its own, or whether it is more deeply embedded as part of the 'normal' ageing process. We do not know the answer yet. But even those who take the view that age-related conditions are distinct disease entities must acknowledge that age is the major factor in how they come about.

The aged organ is more vulnerable to pathology. The aged cell is more liable to dysfunction. But why? The underlying cause of both ageing and disease is the build-up of faults. The extent to which we can isolate the faults that cause Alzheimer's disease from the more general faults that cause other aspects of brain ageing will determine the extent to which we can tackle one without also tackling the other. We have seen great excitement caused by recent reports of a possible therapy for Alzheimer's disease based on a vaccine against the abnormal amyloid-beta peptide associated with this conditon. But the approach has so far been tested only in mice that were genetically engineered to produce brain pathology through the specific deposition of this particular peptide in their brains. They were engineered to arrive at this pathology by a route which does not form a part of the normal ageing of the mouse brain. It remains an open question whether the vaccine can significantly delay disease progression in the normal human brain, where factors other than amyloid-beta are likely to be at work.

It may turn out that, in order to postpone Alzheimer's disease in humans, we need to delay the build-up of several types of damage. Growing evidence shows that age-related degeneration of the blood vessels serving the brain is a factor in Alzheimer's disease. There is evidence, too, that oxidative damage caused by free radicals is an underlying cause. So if we wish to postpone dementia, we will have to slow a process as fundamental to ageing as oxidative damage. What is true for Alzheimer's disease is true for many of the other degenerative conditions associated with ageing. Only by understanding the deeper biochemistry that causes ageing can we understand the molecular and cellular perturbations that lead to age-related disease. It is time to face this reality and its implications.

The idea that normal ageing and age-related diseases share common causes is strongly supported by a great deal of research on the intriguing phenomenon of life extension through calorie restriction. It has been known since the 1930s that if you underfeed a mouse or a rat, but do not subject it to *mal*nourishment, you will extend its life span by as much as 40 or 50 per cent. What is even more striking is that you will also retard the development of an entire spectrum of age-related diseases. We do not know yet if the same approach might work one day in humans, but that is not my point here. My point is that an intervention like calorie restriction in rodents does not affect ageing and disease separately, it affects them in the same way. Some of the latest gene technologies are being used to discover how calorie restriction affects the expression of an animal's

genes. It appears that several genes that cope with molecular damage are tuned to higher levels, something
that we have predicted theoretically. Food restriction
thus causes damage to build up more slowly within the
animals' organs and slows the animals' rate of ageing.
Apart from being lean and hungry, the underfed animals
are all in prime condition – healthy, active and alert –
even at ages when normally fed mice would all be dead.

Faced with such evidence, it seems hard to deny that
there is a direct connection between ageing and disease.
We therefore have to accept that the mantra could be
wrong. If we want to postpone the diseases of old age,
we might not compress morbidity after all, unless we
learn to control the rate of ageing organ by organ and
pick and choose which conditions we would like to
postpone, while leaving ageing in the rest of the organs
to run its normal course. This would be a fundamentally
different approach from that which has driven our revolution to date: the drive to postpone death on all
fronts. Now that we are on the threshold of deep discoveries about the human ageing process, it is important
to open a more informed debate about goals and priorities, as is happening now in a Symposium here at Newcastle's International Centre for Life.

One of the harder questions to address is how we
might wish our own lives to come to a close. Answering this is difficult for several reasons. Firstly, our own
death is not something that we feel comfortable con-

templating, let alone discussing. Secondly, most of us have very limited knowledge of what is actually involved in the later stages of life. Over the last fifty years death has become separate from the mainstream of life, occurring mostly in hospitals or hospices under sanitised conditions. The dead body is rarely laid out at home. How different this is from earlier practice. Thirdly, our opinions alter as our circumstances change. A degree of incapacity that appeared intolerable when we were young may seem much more bearable when in later life we come to experience it. A friend of mine, a North American scientist somewhat older than I, told me how, years ago, he and three of his class-mates swore a solemn oath that in later life they would secretly monitor each other's condition. If a consensus was reached that an individual's intellectual capacity had declined too far, the others were duty-bound to kill him. My friend's great anxiety is that in the intervening years he has lost touch with his friends, but the oath has never been revoked. Although I tell this as a joke, it is not so funny when we consider the far-reaching decisions that may one day be made by others on our behalf.

As we look forward to an era when novel therapies such as stem-cell transfer become feasible, we should give careful thought to how we prefer to end our days. My own particular terror is a drawn-out death from emphysema. But I should not want a sudden, unexpected death either – it is cruel for those who are left behind and I want time to say goodbye. It is less bizarre than it may seem to begin to think in terms of a 'designer death'.

I am not talking here about suicide or euthanasia. Our revolution cannot realistically go on being just a revolution *from* for much longer. If the revolution in the life sciences brings a much greater degree of control over the degenerative diseases, we will acquire the means to direct our revolution *towards* the ends we might choose. I am convinced that developing a greater facility for talking realistically – with less denial – about the end of life will draw some of the sting from ageing and generate a society better equipped psychologically to accommodate the shifting balance of the generations.

Not only must we consider where we want to steer our revolution in terms of the biomedical potential for deferment of disease and prolongation of life, we need also to plan much more imaginatively for an environment in which there will be greatly increased numbers of considerably older people. Many of the issues come under the heading 'enablement' and draw on different dimensions of science and technology.

Last year, I chaired a task force on Healthcare and the Older Person that was charged with anticipating what needs to happen over the next twenty years. We began by looking back over the past twenty years and identifying the things that have changed most since the 1980s. The biggest single change has been the astonishing advance in information technology – computers, mobile phones and the like. This has the potential to revolutionise the lives of older people, but the fact is that the oldest age groups have so far benefited least from IT. The reason is obvious: the industry has made conspicuously little effort to take older people into consideration.

Apart from personal emergency alarms, IT products are directed towards the young. Display fonts are small, buttons fiddly, options complicated. And I am talking here about the middle-aged like myself, let alone those whose vision is impaired or whose manual dexterity is restricted by arthritis. Yet those over sixty-five comprise 20 per cent of our population, many with the financial resources and leisure opportunities to make extensive use of these facilities if they were more accessible. We need many more places on introductory courses, so that older beginners can gain the confidence that this is a technology they can master.

IT can transform the lives of older people, providing contacts, information, entertainment and access to specialised services. It can enable radical new models of health care and support for older people living at home, effecting savings that would amply repay the costs of installing an internet connection in every house, just like electricity, gas and water. But it requires profound changes in attitude – a belief in, and a belief by, older people that they can cope.

Think for a moment how technology has transformed life at the other end of the age spectrum since
the 1980s. Twenty years ago, getting around with
young children was a great deal more awkward than
today. The basic McLaren buggy was the height of
technology then. Child car seats were cumbersome,
often requiring professional fixing. Look at the clever-
ness and choice of today's equivalents! There is no
reason at all, other than attitude, why we have not yet
developed as thriving an industry to cater for the needs
of older people. But even the idea of a motorised
Zimmer frame is seen as a great joke. With different
attitudes, assistive technology can transform lives, creating wealth and job opportunities into the bargain.

Technologies to improve housing, transport and
other essential services offer exciting possibilities to
open new dimensions in older people's lives. It is little
short of tragic that we are not further advanced in trans-
forming such ideas into reality. Admirable pilot schemes
– for example, to develop smart homes for assisted,
independent living – have confirmed the effectiveness
of these novel approaches. The costs are not excessive
and would easily be offset by savings in the traditional,
more burdensome forms of health and social support.
Why are they not mushrooming into full-blown
schemes up and down the country?

We cannot afford to let the turning point in our revolution drift by unheeded or we will find ourselves in

very real difficulties. It may be fortunate, therefore, that change will be driven soon by that oldest of motives – profit. Market forces, particularly in the area of employment, will very soon wake up to the fact that there is going to be a shortage in the work force that can only be filled by recruiting and retaining older workers. Work patterns will have to become more flexible and attractive in order to retain older staff. Jobs and the workplace will require redesign. It is ironic to realise that in all probability it will be profit that will drive the attention to well-being of body and mind in old age that could so easily have been perceived as a priority with less-blinkered eyes. It was shortage of male labour during the First World War that provided the first real advance in the drive to recognise women's rights. It may be the shortage of young labour that will win the first significant battles in the fight against ageism.

But while we can trust market forces and self-interest to help us address some of the challenge of seeking new directions for our revolution, there are areas of life where we must work hard ourselves. I am talking about the spiritual dimension – the personal experience – or, if you like, the *meaning* of our lives. For some, religious belief provides a sufficient framework, a framework in which an older perspective on ageing has been maintained, but which must also adapt to the new. For very many, however, the old religions have no appeal and thin substitutes – in particular, the worship of the body beautiful – have taken their place. It is here that the greatest danger lies. Worshipping the body beautiful is sadly at odds with the realities of ageing. The older body, like the older person, is of course quite as beautiful as the sleek young thing in our magazines or on our screens – more beautiful in many ways, with the added value of a mature character and experience. But unless we learn to see and appreciate this deeper, less superficial, beauty we are doomed to struggle with a progressive and pervasive loss of self-worth as we get older.

It is striking that in recent generations we have lost our sense of the value of an older person's experience, as in Western developed countries we have become obsessed with the excitement of the new. Contrast this with much of Africa and Asia, where the old are still afforded considerable respect. While they adapt from us the technologies to prolong life, cannot we adapt from them fresh ways of structuring our increasingly multi-generational society?

It is not just the general public that has to change its way of seeing the challenge of ageing. The professional outlook of the vast majority of doctors and medical research scientists is founded on the concept of the cure. They don't want to know about ageing because it can't be cured. And yet the geriatrician has some of the finest opportunities to tackle complex and challenging clinical problems of any medical specialism, while research on the ageing process brings the gerontologist face to face with the extraordinary mechanisms that in living cells keep death at bay for so long and against all the odds.

When death of old age comes at the end of a long life, it arrives not because all of our cells are hopelessly shot to pieces but because the fraction of damaged cells quietly passes the threshold for critical failure of one kind or another. Even in a person as old as 100, most of the cells are in good working order. If a cell culture is grown from the biopsied skin of a centenarian, the culture growth rate is not detectably different from that of a culture grown from a much younger person. Our bodies don't just rot. If we can understand more about the fine molecular balance between the processes that lead to damage and the processes that effect repair, there need be no bound to what we can accomplish. Everything we have learned about the science of ageing suggests there is no quick fix – no fountain of youth – but equally there is no limit. With hard work and determination we can keep pushing back the boundaries of good quality life.

In this series of lectures, I challenge science and society to look afresh at what is happening in our world, to recognise the opportunities, as well as the threats to future stability, that stem from the revolution in longevity. I challenge the scientific community to think not only of directing energy towards curing illnesses, but to turn increasingly towards the less glamorous but vital task of helping our ageing cells to guard against the drear damage of the daily grind. I challenge medicine to look in radically new ways at the maintenance of health and quality of life of older people. Can you imagine a world in which the first thing the doctor asks is not your date of birth? I challenge society, collectively and individually, to rethink its attitudes to older people, to recognise the value and beauty of the fact that we are all living so much longer, and to make sacrifices to accommodate those who presume to live on when previously we would have died. Above all, I challenge us all to put an end to age as something that we let get in the way of celebrating all individuals on this earth as true equals.

Part 2

Behind the Headlines

*An inside look at some of the science behind those
promises of eternal youth*

In this section, I take a closer look at some of the recent advances in ageing research that have made front-page news. Behind each story lies an important piece of science, and it is entirely right that such discoveries are brought to public attention. Ageing is the last great mystery in medical science and it is exciting that we are beginning to get insights into why and how it occurs. Nevertheless, like the boy crying 'Wolf', there is a danger in repeated exaggeration. Headlines which claim again and again that scientists have discovered the secret of eternal youth will lead first to boredom and eventually to disillusionment and disbelief. A sceptic might ask why, if science is really on the threshold of making us all live so incredibly long, has it not solved seemingly much simpler problems, like finding a cure for the common cold.

Although some scepticism is justified − comparable advances in other fields do not generate the same fevered reports − the pace of the research is accelerating and the secrets of ageing really are beginning to yield. Powerful techniques are available now that had not been dreamed of ten or twenty years ago. Society needs to keep its finger on the racing pulse of research as firmly and accurately as it can, in order to be prepared for future change. Decisions about the goals and objectives of ageing research, most of which is funded from the public purse, and which is regulated by society's laws, must be taken on an informed basis. The potential applications of new technologies to ageing and age-related diseases raise deep ethical questions. These can be properly addressed only if those involved in the decision-making processes – in a democracy, this includes us all – are sufficiently aware of the actual status of current scientific knowledge.

In the long run, I have high hopes that the advances discussed in this section will lead to spectacular improvements in the health and quality of life of older people, and even to the extension of good quality life itself, but we will need hard work, a measure of luck, and considerable patience.

Drug to make worms live longer

In September 2000, a report in the journal *Science* described a study in which chemically produced antioxidant drugs increased the life spans of small (1 mm long) nematode worms by about 50 per cent, from around twenty days to around thirty days. The worms, of a species called *Caenorhabditis elegans*, ingested the drugs, along with the bacteria on which they fed, from the jelly-like medium on which they were grown. This particular species of worm is used for numerous studies on ageing, since the worms have a naturally short life span and a very simple structure. Experiments can be done quickly, the worms are cheap and easy to rear, and there are few ethical obstacles.

Several factors formed the background to this work. Firstly, an extensive body of evidence has shown that oxidative damage – the accumulation of molecular mischief caused by rogue 'free radical' by-products of the cell's requirement for oxygen – is a significant contributor to the ageing process, not only in worms but also in mammals, birds and insects. Secondly, it was known that several genetic mutations in the same species extend the worm's life span while at the same time increasing its resistance to oxidative stress. Thirdly, earlier work in another commonly used organism, the fruitfly *Drosophila melanogaster*, had shown that if extra copies of the genes for two naturally occurring antioxidant enzymes – superoxide dismutase and catalase – were introduced into the fly's genome, then the levels of these two enzymes in the fly's cells were enhanced and the flies lived longer. Finally, the drugs used in the new worm study were already available as synthetic compounds which had been developed some years earlier by the company Eukarion Inc. to mimic the activities of superoxide dismutase and catalase. These drugs had been shown in a number of animal studies to ameliorate oxidative damage in several disease models where attack by free radicals was thought to be to blame. Thus, there were good grounds to test the hypothesis that the drugs might have antioxidant effects in worms which would result in increased life span.

The experiments confirmed that the drugs did

indeed extend the life span in the worms. This provides further evidence that oxidative damage caused by free radicals is a major determinant of the rate of ageing in this species. Furthermore, it shows that the drugs could be taken up by the worms to produce life span extension without apparently harming the worms in other respects. For example, their egg-laying rate and body size were unaltered.

The significance of the work lies in the fact that free radical damage occurs in all animal species, including humans. Thus, the worm is a 'model' for the possible actions of the same or similar drugs in other species. As far as humans are concerned, the enzymes superoxide dismutase and catalase, whose actions were mimicked by the drugs, are key players in our own antioxidant defences. Therefore, it is tempting to speculate that the same drugs could postpone or ameliorate aspects of human ageing.

Considerable caution is needed, however, before the findings in worms can be extrapolated to humans. The human body is vastly more complex than the worm's, with a much greater array of cell types. The adult worm contains fewer than 1000 somatic cells, none of which undergoes cell division. In the human body, many of our organs and tissues are in a continual state of cell renewal and turnover. There is good evidence that the mechanisms of ageing are correspondingly more complex.

One of the major obstacles to drug discovery is the risk of adverse side-effects, which often do not come to light in simpler models. We know already that the wholesale suppression of free radicals in the human body might have undesirable consequences. Our bodies have learned, during the course of evolution, to use free radicals to advantage; they are used, for example, as part of the weaponry of the immune system and also in the regulation of blood pressure. Thus, if we want to employ artificial free-radical scavengers, like those used in the worm study, to combat ageing, we may need to develop means for highly targeted delivery. We also know that perturbation of the natural network of antioxidant enzymes is not without risk. Superoxide dismutase and catalase are distinct enzymes with distinct roles that need to be kept in balance. Superoxide dismutase converts the superoxide free radical into hydrogen peroxide, which is itself a powerful agent of oxidative damage. Catalase is then required to render the hydrogen peroxide harmless. In Down's syndrome, an extra copy of the gene for superoxide dismutase is carried on the supernumerary chromosome 21, and there is evidence that it is the resulting imbalance in the antioxidant defences of the cell that causes harm. Perturbing the balance of these powerful enzymes may very well have major long-term side-effects in humans that cannot be brought to light in short-term experiments using worms.

Long telomeres in cloned cows

When Dolly the sheep was made by the revolutionary technique of somatic cell cloning in early 1997, much of the scientific community was taken by surprise. Hitherto, it had been thought unlikely that the nucleus from an adult cell, in which many genes had been switched off to produce the necessary specialisation of cell function, could be reprogrammed to start the successful development of a new embryo all over again. In addition to surprise, a key question in scientists' minds was whether Dolly's biological age would reflect only the time that had elapsed since she herself was born, or whether she would be prematurely aged on account of the fact that she was formed from a cell nucleus taken from an adult already several years old. In other words, did somatic cell cloning restore the 'age clock' in the same way as normal reproduction, or not? The answer would be important for potential applications of cloning technology as well as for the science of ageing.

The problem in answering the question of Dolly's real age is the lack of a universal marker of biological age. Recently, however, there has been considerable interest in the possibility that the lengths of structures called telomeres, found at the ends of each of a cell's chromosomes, might serve this role. Dolly's telomeres were found in 1999 to be prematurely short, which seemed rather disappointing. Great excitement therefore greeted a new report in April 2000 that a group of cloned calves not only had longer telomeres than cows which had been conceived naturally, but that their cells also divided more often.

The origins of the telomere story stem from the early 1970s when a Russian scientist, Alexei Olovnikov, first speculated that there might be an intrinsic problem about copying the DNA helix to its very end. The problem is that the normal molecular machinery for DNA replication cannot copy the bit of the helix to which it is attached. Ten years ago it was discovered that the ends of chromosomes − the telomeres − do indeed get progressively shorter as cells divide. It was also discovered that this potentially devastating problem is circumvented in the reproductive cells − the germ-line − by the action of a special enzyme called telomerase. If the cells of the germ-line had not evolved this way around the telomere-shortening problem, life would have gone extinct a long time ago.

A picture began to emerge that is now known as the telomere hypothesis of cellular ageing. In germ cells, telomerase keeps telomeres at a constant length. However, in somatic cells, telomerase gets shut off. Each time a somatic cell divides, its telomeres get shorter. Eventually the telomeres become critically short, resulting in disruption to the mechanisms of cell division and the cell enters a state that is called 'senescence'.

This idea was welcomed by many because it provided a neat mechanism to account for ageing at the cellular level. It also fitted very well with the earlier observation that normal somatic cells can divide only a finite number of times when they are grown in cell culture. Furthermore, the discovery offered valuable insight into the properties of cells grown from malignant tumours. Unlike normal cells, cancer cells can grow without limit. Thus, when it was discovered that in the great majority of human cancers the enzyme telomerase has been 'accidentally' turned back on again, the picture fitted together very nicely. Indeed, I take personal satisfaction in having predicted, in a paper published in *Nature* in 1977, that germ-line immortality is assured by special mechanisms for cellular maintenance that get switched off in normal somatic cells leading to their senescence, but which get turned on again by mistake as part of the cellular dysregulation leading to cancer. At the time telomerase had not been discovered, but its actions fit my idea perfectly.

There is now a great deal of evidence in support of the telomere hypothesis of cellular ageing, including the demonstration in 1998 that introducing a gene that restores telomerase function into normal somatic cells can make them divide indefinitely without showing signs of malignancy. Thus, there is now strong interest in understanding more about the factors that regulate telomere length in the fields of both cancer and ageing. The cloned cow study is interesting for its demonstration that during the process of somatic cell cloning, factors may operate that result in elongation of telomeres, which in turn endows the somatic cells in the cloned animal with a greater division capacity.

A clear note of caution must be sounded, however, about extrapolating from our current understanding of the role of telomeres in cellular ageing to any possible 'fountain of youth' effect. As yet, we have only an incomplete picture about the extent to which the limit on cell division that is imposed by telomere loss contributes to the ageing of the whole organism. We know that telomeres do not shorten in brain and muscle cells, which do not undergo cell division, yet these tissues assuredly age. We also know that the shut-down of telomerase in somatic cells is not as absolute as was first thought. There are cells in the immune system and in the epithelial layers of skin and gut which are required to undergo very large numbers of divisions during a lifetime. In these cells, telomerase is turned back on again under normal circumstances, suggesting that there is more to the regulation of telomere length than was previously thought. The idea that telomere shortening functions as some kind of simple 'ageing clock' is too simplistic.

Although we are beginning to acquire the technology to manipulate the switching on and off of telomerase, in view of the close association between telomerase reactivation and malignancy, we need to be extremely careful about interfering in systems we do not fully understand.

Fly gene doubles life span

A theme that is emerging clearly from a number of independent lines of research is that the regulation of metabolism has important effects on the rate of ageing. This is not too surprising, since we now believe that ageing itself has come about largely because of evolutionary trade-offs between metabolic investments in survival and reproduction. Indeed, the disposable soma theory specifically suggests that we age because at a time when life was brutish and short, it was more important to invest in reproduction than in greater levels of bodily maintenance and repair. As we discover more about the genes that affect life span in model organisms like the worm and fruitfly, we are finding that they are often involved in such fundamental aspects of metabolic regulation as the cellular response to insulin, which controls the utilisation of glucose. The effects of metabolic control on ageing are also connected with the fact that calorie restriction in laboratory rodents increases life span by 30–50 per cent and retards the development of many age-related diseases.

In December 2000, scientists working with the fruitfly discovered a gene whose mutation resulted in a near doubling of life span. A quirky feature of the world of fruitfly genetics is that the discoverer of a new gene can give it more or less any name that he or she wishes (other organisms are subject to stricter naming conventions). Thus, among the descriptive names like *giant*, *hunchback* and *wingless*, we find genes called *sonic hedgehog* or the newly discovered *Indy*, for '*I'm not dead yet*' (by convention, gene names are written in italics).

The major effects of the *Indy* mutation, apart from the increase in life span, are that it alters fat storage and the utilisation of energy. Organisms usually need to do more than spend energy on bodily maintenance and reproduction. In particular, they must store a certain proportion of their surplus energy as fat, in order to tide them over the bad times, when energy supplies may be interrupted or unavailable. *Indy* mutants may turn out to sacrifice their 'rainy day' protection for increased maintenance, which would be fine in the context of the uniform laboratory environment, but less satisfactory in the real world. This would explain why wild fruitfly populations do not carry the mutant form of the gene, since in the natural environment the fly requires all its options for the deployment of metabolic resources to be working.

Given that most genes in fruitflies have homologues (evolutionarily related equivalents) in humans, it may be that *Indy* will provide new clues to metabolic regulation in humans that might allow us to convert surplus energy into longer lives, but it is very early days as yet.

Vaccination against Alzheimer's disease

In December 2000, two studies were reported in the same issue of the journal *Nature*, each describing how immunisation of mice with a vaccine against the amyloid-beta protein that has been implicated in Alzheimer's disease reduced the symptoms of brain damage and cognitive impairment. The hope raised by this work is that a similar approach in humans might allow the development of an effective vaccine to protect against Alzheimer's disease. The fact that two independent studies should have reached similar results at the same time is indicative of the enormous effort that is now being directed at finding effective therapy for Alzheimer's disease.

The mechanisms responsible for Alzheimer's disease have not yet been fully explained, but one of the hallmarks of the disease is the accumulation of lesions called plaques in the brain of an affected person. These plaques contain deposits of amyloid-beta, which is an incomplete version of the normal amyloid protein that is present in all of us. Research in the 1980s showed that in certain families which had an inherited tendency to develop Alzheimer's disease at an unusually early age, there was a mutation in the amyloid gene that led to accelerated deposition of amyloid-beta. Although there has been much controversy about how amyloid-beta fits into the normal development of Alzheimer's disease in the brains of those who lack a genetic predisposition, there is a widely held view that its deposition plays a causal role in the disease process (as opposed to being merely a by-product).

One of the limiting factors in Alzheimer's research until recently has been the lack of suitable animal models, since mice and rats do not develop the disease. Recently, however, transgenic mice have been developed in which mutant forms of the human amyloid gene have been introduced into the mouse genome to produce quantities of amyloid-beta. These animals show progressive deposition of amyloid-beta in their brains associated with cognitive impairment, as assessed by learning and memory tests in a procedure known as the water maze.

The reports in *Nature* described how vaccination of the transgenic mice to produce an immune reaction against the abnormal amyloid-beta protein protected the animals from the impairments of learning and memory associated with the effects of the transgene. The immunised animals also showed reduced deposition of amyloid-beta in their brains.

The obvious exciting feature of these results is that if immunisation can work in mice, it could perhaps achieve a similar result in humans. We must, however, bear in mind certain caveats. In particular, there is evidence in humans that Alzheimer's disease has a complex array of causes. In the transgenic mice, the symptoms were produced by artificially adding a human transgene to the mouse genome in order to produce exactly that form of protein against which the vaccination was targeted. Thus, although the mouse studies demonstrate effectiveness of the immunisation strategy, itself a very exciting result, the result was obtained in an artificially 'clean' system. My worry on this score is reinforced by the fact that in both studies the tests were conducted in relatively young animals (up to six months in one study and up to twelve months in the other). A twelve-month old mouse is roughly equivalent to a thirty-year old human. Research on mouse models of stroke has shown that very different results are obtained when strokes are artificially induced in young animals compared with old. Since Alzheimer's disease does not usually occur in humans until considerably later than thirty years, we don't know yet that the vaccination confers similar protection against the harmful effects of amyloid-beta in later life. Such research will surely be done – the approach is far too promising to hold back.

Regrow your own organs

The last of the advances I consider is the prospect of using embryonic or adult stem cells to replace damaged or dead cells for the treatment of Parkinson's disease, Alzheimer's disease, stroke damage, heart failure and so on. The science is very new and there is a close connection with the ideas of somatic cell cloning.

The essential concept is that all cells in the body carry

the same genes. Whether a cell is a neurone, a heart muscle cell or a white blood cell, for example, the cell's particular identity is controlled by the combinations of genes that are switched on and off. Before Dolly, there was limited expectation that we could reprogramme one kind of cell to take on the functions of another. However, we now see that not only can we manipulate cells from early embryos, in which each cell has the capability of differentiating into any of the specialised types, but we can expect to induce specialised cells to de-differentiate and be reprogrammed. While the ethics of embryo stem-cell research remain an area of intense debate, relatively few ethical objections are raised to the idea of taking stem cells from one's own bone marrow and redirecting these. In fact, many organs (such as skin, gut, muscle, prostate) have their own particular kinds of stem-cells and this list will probably lengthen as more research on stem-cell biology is done.

The problems of directing cell differentiation are likely to be solved – not easily, and probably not for some time, but eventually. What is harder to tell is how far and fast we can expect the *application* of these techniques to advance. It is one thing to direct a cell to become a heart muscle cell. It is quite another to engineer the development of a replacement heart. The key stages of development in a complex organ such as the heart are guided by a combination of (i) highly complicated interactions between neighbouring cells and cell types, (ii) the action of physical forces produced by the fact that the real heart must grow and develop as it works, and (iii) the all-important influence of the network of nerve cells that permeate the heart tissue and connect back to the central nervous system. The first fruits of tissue engineering will be much simpler than whole new organs.

Two issues will limit the application of stem-cell technologies in the domain of ageing. The first is that if we are not to rely on embryonic stem cells, we need to find out much more about how adult stem cells are themselves affected by ageing. Some of my own recent research has been directed at addressing exactly this question. In collaboration with Chris Potten, an expert on the stem cells of the gut, we showed that stem cells in this organ undergo important functional changes with age. Thus, if we want to use adult stem cells for tissue engineering and repair, and if age changes affect the stem cells which we wish to use, we will need to identify and pick only those stem cells which are still good enough for the job. We should remember that every time a cell divides, it must copy its DNA. Every time it copies its DNA there is the likelihood of mutation. Some of these mutations may cause us trouble if we put them back in our bodies. US scientist Bruce Ames – inventor of the widely used 'Ames test' for screening compounds for their potential carcinogenicity – has shown that many active carcinogens are in fact mitogens, that is, they are substances which simply promote cell division and thereby lead to the accumulation of mutations.

We need also to think about the feasibility of effecting repair with stem-cell therapy. In some cases all that we will require is to put intact stem cells of the right kind in the right place. For example, if we can transplant functional insulin-secreting cells into the islets of the pancreas, we may produce a cure for diabetes. However, transplanting functional neurones into a brain ravaged by Alzheimer's disease will not restore the networks of cellular connections in which the lost memories were stored. At best such treatment might restore the capacity to learn anew. This would be by no means a small gain, but it is still far from a full cure.

Part 3

Part 3

Miranda's Tale

*A short story examining the implications
of a world without age*

A Short Story

After five days the Capsule had done its work, and Miranda lay dying. It had been a shock when it had detonated, silently of course, and the world had turned grey. One moment the air taxi, skimming over the northern forests, had been bathed in the rich glow of autumn colours, red, brown and gold, reflecting the low, piercing rays of the newly risen sun. The next moment, or so it had seemed, the sun's gold turned a brilliant white and the forest beneath became a sombre blend of black and greys.

The loss of her colour vision must in reality have taken some minutes to develop, Miranda realised later, but she had been absorbed in her thoughts of the meeting to come and had paid only glancing attention to the glorious view from the window.

The taxi docked at the Quebec terminal and Miranda, thanking the now monochrome driver, had walked the short distance to the little park by the river, the place where she first met Gregor so many years ago, to rethink her plans.

She would of course still attend the meeting of the Council of Timed Ones, which was due to start in half an hour. Her report, incomplete and enigmatic as it was, would not take long to deliver. The Council would find the content unsettling, but as yet there was too little of substance to warrant lengthy discussion. A further study would be authorised, and Miranda could ensure that Juno, her capable deputy, was charged to continue the work of their team. Miranda would be free to leave the Council meeting by early afternoon at the latest, which would allow sufficient time for the air taxi to have her home by nightfall. Inevitably this arrangement meant sacrificing one of her five remaining days to duty, but that would still leave Miranda time to make the necessary arrangements. In many ways, she was glad that the Capsule's detonation, so long awaited, had come while she was busy.

Miranda gazed out over the swirling eddies of the wide river. There was, in truth, little to arrange. Her financial affairs would be settled after her death according to the simple plan she had drawn up long ago. Never one to leave things to the last minute, Miranda had already carefully selected those whom she would invite to attend her dying. The list was a short one. Choosing fitting mementoes for each of them from her small stock of cherished possessions would need careful thought, but even that would not take long. And then, of course, there was Lara.

Lara was the real reason for Miranda's approaching death. And Gregor, too.

Would Gregor have come? Miranda thought, as she watched the silvery light sparkle on a stretch of distant water. Could he have borne it?

Gregor had entered Miranda's life a short time after her ninth fraitch, which, she reflected, would put her in her late 220s. Gregor himself was then nearing his third fraitch, which made him about 150 years her junior. Not that it mattered.

Miranda's love for Gregor had taken her by surprise. It had been immediate and deep, eclipsing the previous loves of her long life. Make no mistake, Miranda's earlier loves had lacked neither warmth nor joy. One of them even resulted in the birth of her cherished son, Nico, now one of her closest friends. But the problem, if problem it had been, was that Miranda had always previously held something important in reserve.

Holding back from full commitment was a habit conditioned by the boundless possibilities of an unlimited future. The only known strategy to cope with this awesome prospect, short of mind-numbing drugs and escapist diversions, was to cultivate and preserve an exaggerated love of oneself. In the early centuries after fraitch technology was developed, the emotional burden of long life was poorly understood and the suicide rate grew alarmingly high. Psycho-fraitching of the mind quickly became as important as the regeneration of the cells and tissues of the body.

After their first meeting by the river, and during the heady weeks that followed, Miranda had been startled to discover that Gregor loved her with an intensity and passion that went way beyond all of her previous experience. Not short of passion herself, Miranda found her reserve and self-absorption melting away. She delighted in Gregor's presence and he in hers. When Miranda gave up her farmland home to live permanently in the limestone caves where Gregor had carved his beautiful dwelling, her friends were jolted with the shock. With the quaint exception of the Snuggees, a near invisible sect that inhabited the far north-east and practised, so it was said, the bizarre habit of 'family living', most individuals preferred to live alone, meeting by choice to share bounded periods of time.

Fifteen full and happy years passed quickly in Miranda's and Gregor's lives, their time occupied with creative work and play. During these years, Miranda's love for Gregor had grown ever stronger and deeper, until the day finally came that Miranda made the decision which would alter their lives for ever. Miranda decided that she wanted to share with Gregor the making of a child.

In a world freed from the necessity of ageing, the making of children had very great significance. Children were still needed to replace those who died from accidents or suicides, but the accidental death rate was so small that their production had to be strictly controlled. The method was simple and stark. Each individual at birth was genetically screened and assigned the right to share in the making of a certain number of children. The usual number was two, but sometimes a smaller number was awarded to limit the spread of harmful genotypes. Exceptionally, a person might be allowed three children if, for example, the recent toll of accidents had been unusually great. The bonus of a third child was awarded by random selection.

To guard against abuse of the quota system and to protect against possible genetic damage to the reproductive cells, which might have a very long wait before use, all fertilisations were carried out *in vitro* from stored germ cells. Once sufficient germ cells had been removed to cold storage, the gonads were rendered sterile.

To share in the making of a child, a couple would declare their request in a civil ceremony of great solemnity, and following rigorous checks on quota status and genetic compatibility, the fertilisation would be performed. The resulting embryo would then be raised to term either within the womb of the mother or, as was increasingly the custom, in a foetal incubator.

For a person with a quota of two, like Miranda, the making of a first child was without major consequence. The parents might choose to participate closely in the rearing of the infant, or they might spend only occasional time with their child, as they preferred. They might do so jointly or, more usually, as individuals. A greater preoccupation with self had weakened the traditional bonding of parents with each other and with their child. In the interests of all, it had become both custom and law that the primary responsibility for the welfare and education of the child rested with the community of which the child would, in due course, become a long-term participant.

However, the making of the final child of a person's quota was an entirely different matter. The birth of this last child signalled the parent's forfeiture of the right to any further fraitches beyond an immediate and final one, at the completion of which a Capsule was implanted. This terminal fraitch delivered the same rejuvenatory effects of the earlier fraitches, but the implanted Capsule imposed a delayed sentence of death. At a random point in time, between forty and fifty years from the date of implantation, the Capsule would detonate, causing the release of a sequence of neurotoxins that would bring painless death in five days. Any attempt at surgical removal of the Capsule would trigger immediate detonation. The bearer of such a Capsule became a Timed One.

It was this fate that Miranda elected for herself when she decided to make a child with Gregor.

Whether Gregor truly understood the nature of Miranda's choice at that time, Miranda never knew. A proposal to share in the making of a child was the deepest token that could be offered to a partner. By custom, each partner's motives for making and either accepting or declining such proposals were respected as the individual and private concern only of the other. Good manners forbade questioning. Rigid convention held that a person's reproductive quota was their own personal secret. Perhaps Gregor persuaded himself that Miranda was lucky enough to have a quota of three, for he knew Nico, her son, well.

But after Lara, their daughter, was born and Miranda adopted the white sash of a Timed One, the light had seemed to leave Gregor's life. Then, a week before Lara's second birthday, had been the accident. Gregor, always more of a risk-taker than most, had gone flying with his sailwing over the Middle Mountains and not returned. By the time his broken body was discovered in a rock-strewn gully two days later, his organs were beyond the repair of even the most skilled of the regenerators.

And so had begun the final phase of Miranda's life, in which, as a Timed One, she had access to the Great Archive and began the work she had grown to love.

During her first months in the Archive, Miranda had

immersed herself thoroughly in the history of the Dark Years. She read how the scientists of the late twentieth century had at last begun to understand the ageing of the body and had groped their way with crude tools and glimmerings of insight into the deep mysteries of development and regeneration. She marvelled at the progress that had been made, in spite of primitive techniques, during the middle decades of the twenty-first century in the postponement of some of the worst sufferings of old age. She read with incredulity of the war between the maximalists, who valued life extension above all else, and the utilitists, who wanted to impose a crude yardstick by which quality and productivity of life could be measured, with euthanasia applied to those whose tally was negative. She learned of the brutal triumph of the utilitists in certain eastern regions, where the structures of society had finally broken down under the weight of the demographic revolution, reinforced by the consequences of harsh fertility control. Too few young people could not keep the traditional systems going, and in truth felt little obligation to do so. She read disbelievingly of the devastating competition among private corporations, in which each sought to exploit scientific discoveries for amassing personal wealth. And she read despairingly of the Cataclysm that befell the world when the strains became too much and, in the early years of the twenty-second century, economic and social order broke down altogether.

Ironically, it had been the quest for eternal youth that caused the deaths of so many. Life spans had continued to inch upwards as the diseases of old age were brought increasingly under control. These diseases were not eliminated, of course, but their onset was postponed, and the numbers of those celebrating their hundredth birthdays had grown and grown. But ageing itself had not been affected, and still no one had lived past 130 years.

Then came word of a breakthrough. A remarkable success by a small and secretive research laboratory, Timespan Inc., had engineered mice that, it was claimed, lived twice the normal life span. No special procedures, like near-starvation diets, were needed to produce these long lives. The key lay in the controlled renewal and regeneration of tissues from cryopreserved cells.

Application to humans remained a distant prospect, however. Even the research that might make this faint prospect a reality was deemed morally unacceptable by the World Council on Ethics. Undaunted, Timespan Inc. built a second research facility on a remote stretch of the Caribbean coast of Central America under the guise of an exclusive health colony, and began the clandestine recruitment of human clients.

In spite of the intense secrecy with which Timespan shrouded its operations, it became known that a small but growing number of the world's richest people had withdrawn, apparently permanently, from society.

Rumour spread that they had joined an immortal élite at the Timespan colony. An angry groundswell of public opinion sought to force an inspection of the colony by the World Council on Ethics. While the Council's members debated the issue at length, a direct invasion of the colony was organised by VuNews, the largest of the news corporations, citing overriding public interest as just cause. The results were horrific. Rejuvenation had worked in part, but the control of cell proliferation was imperfect, and gross deformities had resulted. Worse still, rejuvenation of brain function had been a total failure. The mutilated and often demented clients remained voluntary prisoners in the Timespan colony, awaiting the promised refinements that might relieve their sufferings.

The refinements never came. Instead, the universal horror and revulsion produced by the VuNews broadcasts created an atmosphere in which a long-smouldering resentment of scientific interference, as many deemed it, with the natural world, suddenly caught flame. Fanned by the rhetoric of charismatic leaders and armed by a motley assortment of anti-establishment militias, a violent outbreak of hostility was directed at all that could be identified as the product of science and technology. A three-day orgy of rioting and mass destruction disrupted power systems, transport networks and communications equipment across the world.

The records of what happened next were scant, Miranda found. The material damage cannot, in absolute terms, have been very great, but it was more extensive than had ever been envisaged. Few had appreciated until then the knife edge along which the civilised world had advanced, as a remorseless drive for greater and greater technological efficiency had cut away the capacity to recover from such a comprehensive breakdown. Before order could be restored, a disastrous destabilisation occurred. Panicking citizens stripped city stores of their food stocks, and the supplies of fuel for vehicles were drained dry. With no prospect of further supplies being delivered, and with looting and violence spreading, an exodus began that the police and armed forces sought unsuccessfully to control. Those not killed in skirmishes with refugees and looters soon realised the futility of trying to stem the tide and joined the great escape. But escape to what? Rural districts set about defending themselves, their crops and their livestock, but soon they too were overwhelmed. Machine-intensive farming ground to a halt. It was later estimated, Miranda read, that one-tenth of the world's 6 billion inhabitants died in that first desperate month. Three-quarters of the rest did not survive another year, falling victim to cold, hunger, drought or raging epidemics of disease.

Gradually, the remnants of the human race rebuilt a life of sorts. But it was a grim time indeed. Even in the more lately developed regions of Africa and Asia, traditional farming skills had been abandoned two generations or more ago. The terrible mistakes of history repeated themselves. Potatoes, quick and easy to grow, sustained many a community until a new blight revealed again the perilous dangers of monoculture. Millions died in the American potato famines of the 2130s.

Fortunately, a few hard-copy libraries had been preserved through the electronic age, more as historical curios than as practical sources of information. Of these, the collection at the National Library of Medicine near the ruined city of Washington proved the most valuable. Desperate to restore genetic diversity and to breed crops and animals better suited for traditional agriculture, the farmers of the new era immersed themselves in the study of all aspects of biology. Machines were discouraged although not outlawed, provided that lack of critical dependence on mechanisation could be demonstrated. Most important, a thorough working knowledge in at least one branch of the sciences was deemed an essential qualification for citizenship of any of the newly emerging societies.

The harnessing of so much intellectual power to the pursuit of science led to important advances, and the sound application of new discoveries was greatly aided by the deepened public understanding of the issues at stake. Ethical assessment was an integral component of each programme of research and development, and the involvement of the wider community was easily secured.

Miranda had been almost amused to read in the archives the accounts of the clumsy ethical debates that had occurred, particularly in the latter half of the twentieth century, when non-scientists who eschewed the need to learn science had struggled to understand what the scientists were really aiming to do, and the scientists, so immured in their own narrow researches, were almost equally unappreciative of the worries and misapprehensions that troubled their fellow citizens. Of course, it had not really been funny, Miranda acknowledged. The seeds of the Cataclysm had lain in such divisions, waiting only upon the conditions for their eventual germination.

In the area of medicine, the greatest advances came first in the new cures of cancers, founded as they were in a precise understanding of what it was that made the cancer cells divide and spread. Different cancers needed different cures, but at last they were all brought under control. From the control of cell proliferation came the ability to induce the repair of damaged or amputated limbs, through precise manipulation of regenerative stem cells. The hardest challenge had been the repair of the spinal cord and brain, but in the end even this had been possible.

It was around this time, Miranda had already known,

that the first research team had begun seriously to work on a prototype of the fraitch. As any high school student knew, fraitch technology was based on stem cells. More complicated was the way that the stem cells were induced to migrate through the body to find their 'shadows', the pre-existing stem cells within the target tissues. The infusion of the molecular signal that would cause the new stem cells to activate the self-destruct signals on the surfaces of their shadows, and then to engulf and digest their dying remains, was the real moment at which the fraitch took place. No matter how many times Miranda had struggled through the relevant chapter in her textbooks, she knew she still did not really grasp how the renewal of the nerve cells of the brain took place. It was similar to shadowing, but the much harder part was how the new nerve cells were guided to make the same connections with other cells, thus preserving the memories and identity of the person being fraitched.

'Too late to fix that now,' Miranda thought, but she knew that the nerve cell renewal remained the least secure aspect of the fraitch. It was estimated that a good fraitch restored at least 99 per cent of the earlier brain cell connections. The 1 per cent that failed to get reconnected right made for some slight discontinuity, which Miranda knew from experience could be a little unsettling. On the other hand, there were those who liked this element of novelty in a fraitch. By convention, those nearest and most important to you would drop anything if invited to be with you in the days after a fraitch in order to help restore lost memories. They do the same for a dying, of course, thought Miranda wryly.

The early fraitches had been done with stem cells taken from the body, screened in the test tube, and cryopreserved. Now, of course, they took the cells from your embryo before you were born. In fact, they took the cells even before the embryo began to differentiate into its different organs and tissues. That way the cells kept the maximum capacity for growth and differentiation, and were as free as possible from the damage that began to accumulate as soon as the somatic tissues were formed. The cells for your own future fraitches were taken from your embryo even before they took the germ cells that might eventually be used to make your babies.

The population problem had been foreseen at once. This was when the idea of limited reproduction and Timed Ones was adopted. No one had really objected to the idea that indefinite life span needed to be sacrificed for the opportunity to reproduce. Why, it even mimicked the reason that ageing had evolved in the first place, but for a rather different reason. The evolution of ageing had followed the Darwinian imperative in a world where life was risky and reproduction must be afforded a higher priority than a durable soma. In our own world, Miranda mused, life has become so secure that the luxury of reproduction must be paid for by the giving up of life.

At first, Timed Ones were simply denied further fraitches, condemning them to undergo the customary ageing process. But as ageing became less and less a part of the collective memory, it was decreed that to let someone age was a cruel and unusual punishment, and the first Capsules were used. Once again, some trial and error had been needed. The first Capsules were crude affairs that simply detonated at a precisely timed date to cause sudden death. Living with the knowledge of one's date of death had proved insufferable, as Miranda found had been well known in the barbaric days when certain regions of the world still punished criminals with execution. So the time-window Capsule was developed with the forty to fifty year randomiser. A Timed One now held a solemn public farewell at the fortieth anniversary of Capsule implantation and thereafter lived, as Miranda had done, knowing that death could, at any time during the next ten years, occur within five days. The five-day period had been agreed as providing the best compromise between too sudden and too protracted a dying. The contents of the Capsule had also been modified to ensure a painless but progressive loss of faculties, so that death, when it came on the fifth day, was not too unwelcome an intruder.

'Why forty to fifty years?' Miranda had once asked, but she understood the reasons clearly enough now. An early communal decision had been made to entrust the highest executive powers to the Timed Ones, in the knowledge that they alone lacked vested interest in manipulating society to their individual long-term advantage. In some ways, they were like the councils of elders of the ancient times. Forty years was necessary to ensure continuity of government and to give time for the ablest Timed Ones to be elected to, and serve on, the Council. But also, Miranda had noticed with shock when she saw her reflection in a mirror a year ago, it was because forty years was long enough for the early signs of ageing to reveal themselves. She had been amazed when she caught sight of her first grey hair, and in the weeks that followed, she had run her fingers wonderingly over the beginnings of the first tiny wrinkles in the soft skin at the base of her neck.

What will Lara make of that? thought Miranda. Lara had always seemed to her a bit of a cold fish. Miranda had secretly felt a small hurt, but no great surprise, that Lara appeared repelled by Miranda's status as a Timed One and that she showed no acknowledgement of the sacrifice that had permitted her own being.

Five years after becoming a Timed One, when her perusal of the Great Archive had told her much that she had wanted to know, Miranda had been invited to join in one of the Special Projects that concerned the future of the race.

The Special Projects were not, of course, the

province of the Timed Ones alone. There were too few Timed Ones to make this feasible and the research needed long application of effort. But each Special Project was directed by a team of three Timed Ones, who recruited replacements as the need arose. One of the Special Projects was concerned with the worrying tendency in individuals, after a number of fraitches, for their bodies to grow misaligned. Limbs curved, or were of slightly differing lengths. Organs grew slightly out of proportion. Surgery could repair most of these defects, but a surer measure to correct the drift of the body plan was desired.

Another Special Project considered the problem of mutation in stem cells grown in the test tube. To date, the number of fraitches undergone by the longest-lived individuals had not severely tested the biotechnological capabilities of the cell technicians, but the time would undoubtedly come when the mutation question would have to be solved, especially since natural selection, with its 'purifying' action to eliminate deleterious mutations, was now effectively inoperative. But could a force as fundamental as natural selection really be neutralised?

This was the question that prompted Miranda's eventual choice of Special Project. The world's population size was strictly controlled at a comfortable 100 million, large enough to maintain diversity and farm the arable lands, but small enough to manage without crowding or intensive agriculture. Mating was largely by random individual choice and monitored for genetic compatibility. The former races had merged, but diversity of colour, shape and size continued, favoured by a culture of unprecedented harmony and tolerance. The choosing of the time and partner for making a child was governed by many factors, none of which had so far revealed a discernible pattern. But lately, Miranda had learned, a new trend was appearing. People were choosing to make children earlier. And not only were first children being made earlier, but second ones too. The age at which people were becoming Timed Ones was growing younger. The trend was not yet statistically significant in view of the smallness of the sample, but it was definitely suggestive.

If the trend was genuine, was it caused by a genetic or a psychological change? This was the question that Miranda's Special Project had been addressing.

Not my Special Project any more, mused Miranda. But I would have liked to know. It had intrigued her that, if the trend was real, and continued, life spans would grow shorter again. The human race might even evolve to conform to the old fallacious idea that each of us has a reproductive duty to the species and that when this is fulfilled it is time for us to age and die. Miranda chuckled silently to herself at this quaint thought.

Only a few hours left, she thought, and slowly opened her eyes. The room, dimmer now, was as it had been before her reverie. Nico was sitting quietly, close beside her couch. Helen, Prato and Cesar, friends of many, many years, were watching from across the room. 'But where is Lara?' Miranda muttered crossly. 'She ought to be here by now.'

A noise of the door opening disturbed the silence and all at once there was Lara, beautiful as ever. Miranda was sad, suddenly, that she could no longer see the red gleam of Lara's long hair, its colour inherited from Gregor, whose tangled locks and beard had always flamed in the light of the sun.

'Forgive me, I am late,' Lara said directly to Miranda, and Miranda could not help but notice the shudder of distaste with which Lara took in Miranda's occasional grey hair and the fine wrinkles that now showed more clearly on Miranda's skin. 'I hope you will not mind, but I have brought Frederic.'

The shock Miranda felt must have revealed itself on her face. To bring a stranger to a dying was unthinkable. For a moment Lara looked painfully awkward, but her face softened into a nervous smile. 'I wanted him to meet you. We are making a child together.'

Miranda closed her eyes with a soft smile and the room was still.

Bibliography

Social and economic perspectives

Barry, R. L., Bradley, G. V. (eds.). *Set No Limits: A Rebuttal to Daniel Callahan's Proposal to Limit Health Care for the Elderly*. University of Illinois Press, Chicago, 1991.

Bell, E., et al. *Ageing in OECD Countries: a Critical Policy Challenge*. OECD, Paris, 1996.

Bernard M., et al (ed.). *Women Ageing*. Routledge, London, 2000.

Blaikie, A. *Ageing and Popular Culture*. Cambridge University Press, Cambridge, 1999.

Bond, J. *Ageing in Society*. Sage Publications Ltd, London, 1993

Creedy, J. (ed.). *The Economics of Ageing*. Edward Elgar, Aldershot, 1995.

Harper, S. *Ageing Societies*. Arnold, London, 2000.

Johnson, J., Slater, R. *Ageing and Later Life*. Sage, London, 1993.

Laslett, P. *A Fresh Map of Life*. Weidenfeld & Nicolson, London, 1989.

OECD. *Maintaining Prosperity in an Ageing Society*. OECD, Paris, 1998

Simmons, N. (ed.). *Getting a Life: Older People Talking*.

Peter Owen, London, 2000.

Tout, K. *Ageing in Developing Countries*. Oxford University Press, Oxford, 1989.

United Nations. *Ageing and the Family: Proceedings of the United Nations International Conference on Ageing Populations in the Context of the Family*. United Nations, New York, 1994.

Walker, A., Maltby, T. *Ageing Europe*. Open University Press, Milton Keynes, 1996.

Wilson, G. *Global Perspectives on Ageing*. Sage, London, 2000.

Biological and medical perspectives

Arking, R. *Biology of Aging: Observations and Principles*. Prentice-Hall, Englewood Cliffs, 1991.

Austad, S. N. *Why We Age*. John Wiley & Sons, New York, 1998.

Bock, G. and Goode, J. (eds.). *Ageing Vulnerability: Causes and Interventions*. John Wiley and Sons, Chichester, 2001.

Cairns, J. *Matters of Life and Death*. Princeton University Press, New Jersey, 1997.

Ebrahim, S. and Kalache, A. (eds.). *Epidemiology in Old Age*. BMJ Publishing Group, London, 1996.

Evans, J. G., Williams, T. F., Beattie, B. L., Michel, J.-P. and Wilcock, G. K. (eds.). *Oxford Textbook of Geriatric Medicine*, 2nd edn. Oxford University Press, Oxford, 2000.

Finch, C. E. *Longevity, Senescence and the Genome*. University of Chicago Press, Chicago, 1990.

Finch, C. E. and Kirkwood, T. B. L. *Chance, Development and Ageing*. Oxford University Press, New York, 2000.

Hayflick, L. *How and Why We Age*. Ballantine Books, New York, 1994.

Holliday, R. *Understanding Ageing*. Cambridge University Press, Cambridge, 1995.

Huppert, F. A., Brayne, C. and O'Connor, D. W. (eds.). *Dementia and Normal Ageing*. Cambridge University Press, Cambridge, 1994.

Kirkwood, T. B. L. *Time of Our Lives: The Science of Human Ageing*. Phoenix Press, London, 2000.

Marinker, M. (ed.). *Controversies in Health Care Policies: Challenges to Practice*. BMJ Publishing Group, London, 1994.

Rattan, S. I. S. and Toussaint, O. (eds.). *Molecular Gerontology: Research Status and Strategies*. Plenum Press, New York, 1996.

Ricklefs, R. E. and Finch, C. E. *Aging: A Natural History*. Scientific American Library, New York, 1995

Robine, J.-M., Kirkwood, T. B. L. and Allard, M. (eds.). *Sex and Longevity: Sexuality, Gender, Reproduction, Parenthood*. Springer-Verlag, Berlin, 2001.

Robine, J.-M., Vaupel, J. W., Jeune, B. and Allard,

M. (eds.). *Longevity: To the Limits and Beyond.*
Springer-Verlag, Berlin, 1997.

Rowe, J. W. and Kahn, R. L. *Successful Aging.*
Pantheon, 1998.

Smith, D. W. E. *Human Longevity.* Oxford University
Press, New York, 1993.

Stuart-Hamilton, I. *The Psychology of Ageing.* Jessica
Kingsley, London, 2000.

Tallis, R. C, Fillit, H. M. and Brocklehurst, J. C.
(eds.). *Brocklehurst's Textbook of Geriatric Medicine,*
5th edn. Churchill Livingstone, Edinburgh, 1998.

te Velde, E. R., Pearson, P. L. and Broekmans, F. J.
(eds.). *Female Reproductive Ageing.* Parthenon
Publishing, Carnforth, 2000.

Quoted research articles

Janus, C., Pearson, J., McLaurin, J., Mathews, P. M.,
Jiang, Y., Schmidt, S. D., Chishti, M. A., Horne,
P., Heslin, D., French, J., Mount, H. T. J., Nixon,
R. A., Mercken, M., Bergeron, C., Fraser, P. E., St
George-Hyslop, P. and Westaway, D. 'A beta
peptide immunization reduces behavioural
impairment and plaques in a model of Alzheimer's
disease.' *Nature* 408:979–82, 2000.

Lanza, R. P., Cibelli, J. B., Blackwell, C., Cristofalo,
V. J., Francis, M. K., Baerlocher, G. M., Mak, J.,
Schertzer, M., Chavez, E. A., Sawyer, N.,
Lansdorp, P. M. and West, M. D. 'Extension of cell

life-span and telomere length in animals cloned from senescent somatic cells.' *Science* 288:665–9, 2000.

Melov, S., Ravenscroft, J., Malik, S., Gill, M. S., Walker, D. W., Clayton, P. E., Wallace, D. C., Malfroy, B., Doctrow, S. R. and Lithgow, G. J. 'Extension of life-span with superoxide dismutase/catalase mimetics.' *Science* 289:1567–9, 2000.

Morgan, D., Diamond, D. M., Gottschall, P. E., Ugen, K. E., Dickey, C., Hardy, J., Duff, K., Jantzen, P., DiCarlo, G., Wilcock, D., Connor, K., Hatcher, J., Hope, C., Gordon, M. and Arendash, G. W. 'A beta peptide vaccination prevents memory loss in an animal model of Alzheimer's disease.' *Nature* 408:982–5, 2000.

Rogina, B., Reenan, R. A., Nilsen, S. P. and Helfand, S. L. 'Extended life-span conferred by cotransporter gene mutations in *Drosophila*.' *Science* 290:2137–40, 2000.

Shanley, D. P. and Kirkwood, T. B. L. 'Evolution of the human menopause.' *BioEssays* 23:282–7, 2001.

Index